SPOTLIGHT · ON LITERACY ·

Authors, Consultants, and Reviewers

MULTICULTURAL AND EDUCATIONAL
CONSULTANTS

Alma Flor Ada, Yvonne Beamer, Joyce Buckner,
Helen Gillotte, Cheryl Hudson, Narcita Medina,
Lorraine Monroe, James R. Murphy, Sylvia Peña,
Joseph B. Rubin, Ramon Santiago, Cliff Trafzer,
Hai Tran, Esther Lee Yao

LITERATURE CONSULTANTS

Ashley Bryan, Joan I. Glazer, Paul Janeczko,
Margaret H. Lippert

INTERNATIONAL CONSULTANTS

Edward B. Adams, Barbara Johnson,
Raymond L. Marshall

MUSIC AND AUDIO CONSULTANTS

John Farrell, Marilyn C. Davidson,
Vincent Lawrence, Sarah Pirtle, Susan R. Synder,
Rick and Deborah Witkowski, Eastern Sky Media
Services, Inc.

TEACHER REVIEWERS

Terry Baker, Jane Bauer, James Bedi, Nora Bickel,
Vernell Bowen, Donald Cason, Jean Chaney,
Carolyn Clark, Alan Cox, Kathryn DesCarpentrie,
Carol L. Ellis, Roberta Gale, Brenda Huffman,
Erma Inscore, Sharon Kidwell, Elizabeth Love,
Isabel Marcus, Elaine McCraney, Michelle Moraros,
Earlene Parr, Dr. Richard Potts, Jeanette Pulliam,
Michael Rubin, Henrietta Sakamaki,
Kathleen Cultron Sanders, Belinda Snow,
Dr. Jayne Steubing, Margaret Mary Sulentic,
Barbara Tate, Seretta Vincent,
Willard Waite, Barbara Wilson, Veronica York

Macmillan/McGraw-Hill

A Division of The McGraw·Hill Companies

Copyright © 2000, 1999 McGraw-Hill School Division,
a Division of the Educational and Professional
Publishing Group of The McGraw-Hill Companies, Inc.

McGraw-Hill School Division
Two Penn Plaza
New York, New York 10121
Printed in the United States of America

ISBN 0-02-185880-2 / 3, L. 8

2 3 4 5 6 7 8 9 071 03 02 01 00 99

Spotlight on Literacy

AUTHORS

ELAINE MEI AOKI • VIRGINIA ARNOLD • JAMES FLOOD • JAMES V. HOFFMAN • DIANE LAPP

MIRIAM MARTINEZ • ANNEMARIE SULLIVAN PALINCSAR • MICHAEL PRIESTLEY • CARL B. SMITH

WILLIAM H. TEALE • JOSEFINA VILLAMIL TINAJERO • ARNOLD W. WEBB • KAREN D. WOOD

Macmillan McGraw-Hill

NEW YORK • FARMINGTON

Unit 1

Good Thinking!

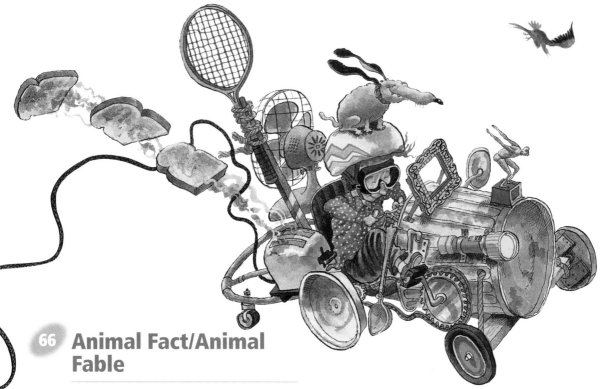

Unit 2

See for Yourself

Unit 3

Family Album

8

Unit 1

The Little Painter

Meet Patricia Maloney Markun

Patricia Maloney Markun was born and raised in Minnesota. After her marriage, she moved to Panama. She lived there for nineteen years.

In Panama she met Fernando, the boy in *The Little Painter of Sabana Grande*. Markun traveled two days over very rough roads to his tiny village. Seeing Fernando's beautiful paintings, Markun was glad she made the hard trip. Years later, she decided to write a book about him.

Meet Robert Casilla

The Little Painter of Sabana Grande is a favorite of illustrator Robert Casilla. He says, "I related to the story because I too am an artist." Casilla also liked the story because of its Hispanic setting.

Casilla says, "I love doing children's books. There is something magic about them. I like the idea my book will get into a child's hands and communicate a message."

# of Sabana Grande

Written by Patricia Maloney Markun   Illustrated by Robert Casilla

igh in the mountains of Panama lies the village of Sabana Grande. It is very small. Just seven houses of clay adobe stand alongside a brook in a grassy meadow. In the middle house lives the Espino family.

At dawn one cool purple morning, the rooster next door crowed. The Espinos woke up.

Papa went off to the meadow to milk the cow.

Mama stirred up the fire in the open-air kitchen and fried golden breakfast tortillas.

Fernando rolled up his straw sleeping mat and put it in the corner. He hurried to the kitchen to eat his tortilla right away.

This was an important day. At school Fernando had learned to draw colored pictures with crayons. Now school was out for dry-season vacation, and Fernando was going to paint for the first time.

His teacher, Señora Arias, had told him exactly how the country people of Panama made their paints. She said:

"Black from the charcoal of a burned tree stump.
Blue of certain berries that grow deep in the jungle.
Yellow from dried grasses in the meadow.
And red from the clay on the bottom of the brook."

It took him a long time to make the paints. Black was easy, because the burned stump of a big tree lay right next to the Espinos' adobe house.

But Fernando had to look and look before he found those certain berries deep in the jungle, to make the blue paint.

In the corner of the meadow he found a patch of very dry grass, and from that he made a large pot of yellow.

He wandered up and down alongside the brook, looking for clay. The fast-flowing water was too deep for him to reach down to the bottom. At last he came to a bend in the brook where the water was shallow. He reached down and dug up a fistful of clay. It was red, just the way Señora Arias had said.

17

Now his paints were stirred up and waiting—black, blue, yellow, and red, in four bowls. Next he got out the three paintbrushes his teacher had given him—one very small, one medium-sized, and one especially large.

I'm ready to paint pictures, Fernando said to himself. He picked up the small brush and dipped it into the pot of red. Then he had a terrible thought.

He had nothing to paint a picture on! An artist needs paper.

He looked in both rooms of the house. He could find no paper at all.

He ran from house to house asking everyone in Sabana Grande for paper to paint on. None of the neighbors had any. Not a scrap.

Fernando was sad. After all his work he wouldn't be able to paint pictures—the colored pictures he could almost see, he wanted to make them so badly. Paints and brushes weren't enough. He needed paper, too.

His fingers itched to draw something—anything. He put
down the paintbrush and went over to the mud by the brook.
He picked up a stick and drew in the wet dirt, the way he had
ever since he was a very little boy.

The big rooster who woke him every morning came out of
the chicken yard next door. Fernando looked at him and drew
the shape of a rooster. He sighed. He couldn't use his new red
and yellow paints to make a bright rooster. He couldn't make the
rooster's comb red. He could only scratch out a mud-colored
rooster. It wasn't the same as painting would be. It didn't have
any color.

Fernando looked around at the adobe houses of his village. Suddenly he got an idea. Adobe was smooth and white—almost like paper. Why couldn't he paint on the outside of his family's adobe house?

"No!" Papa said. "Who ever saw pictures on the outside of a house?"

"No!" Mama agreed. "What would the neighbors say?"

Fernando looked at his pots of paint and was very unhappy. He wanted to paint pictures more than anything else he could think of.

At last Papa said, "I can't stand to see my boy so miserable. All right, Fernando. Go ahead and paint on the house!"

Mama said, "Do your best, Fernando. Remember, the neighbors will have to look at your pictures for a very long time."

First Fernando made a tiny plan of the pictures he was going to paint, painting it with his smallest brush on one corner of the house.

"Your plan looks good to me, Fernando," Papa said. "If you can paint pictures small, you should be able to paint them big."

Fernando picked up his bigger brushes and started to paint a huge picture of the most beautiful tree in Panama, the flowering poinciana, on the left side of the front door. As he painted, he could look up and see the red flowers of a poinciana tree, just beginning its dry season, blooming on the mountainside.

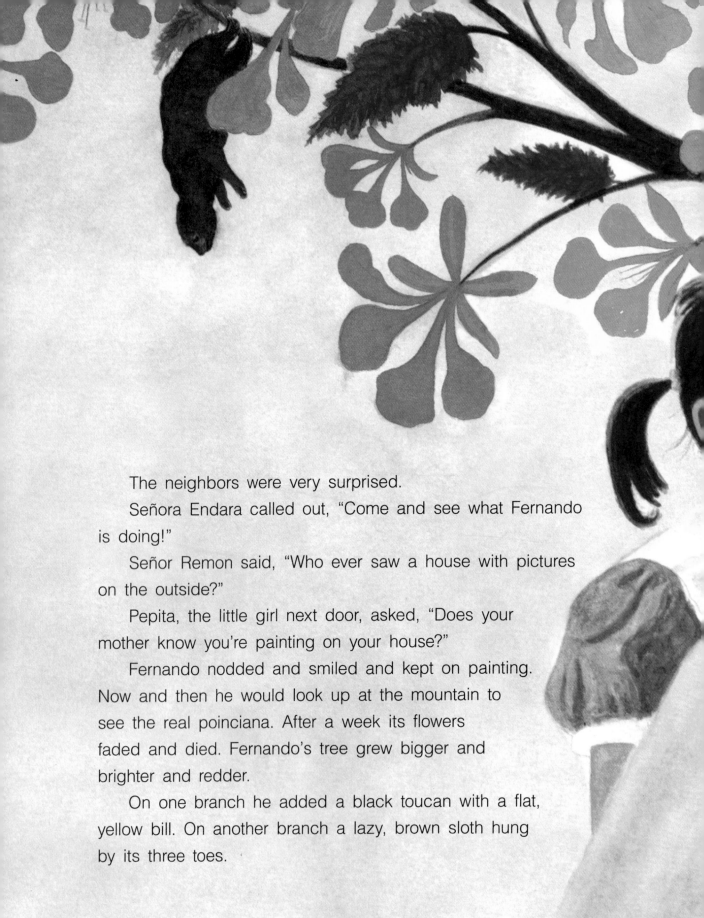

The neighbors were very surprised.

Señora Endara called out, "Come and see what Fernando is doing!"

Señor Remon said, "Who ever saw a house with pictures on the outside?"

Pepita, the little girl next door, asked, "Does your mother know you're painting on your house?"

Fernando nodded and smiled and kept on painting. Now and then he would look up at the mountain to see the real poinciana. After a week its flowers faded and died. Fernando's tree grew bigger and brighter and redder.

On one branch he added a black toucan with a flat, yellow bill. On another branch a lazy, brown sloth hung by its three toes.

The neighbors brought out chairs. While Fernando worked, they drank coffee and watched him paint.

Next he painted the wall on the other side of the door. An imaginary vine with flat, green leaves and huge, purple blossoms crept up the wall.

Word spread about the little painter of Sabana Grande. Even people from Santa Marta, the village around the mountain, hiked into town to watch him paint. The purple vine now reached almost to the thatched roof.

One day Señora Arias came from the school in Santa Marta. Why was his teacher looking for him, Fernando wondered. It was still dry season, when there wasn't any school. It hadn't rained for a month.

"School's not starting yet," his teacher said. "I came to see your painted adobe house that everyone in Santa Marta is talking about. Fernando, you did very well with those paintbrushes. I like it!"

She turned to the neighbors. "Don't you?"

"We certainly do!" the neighbors agreed.

They poured some coffee for the visiting teacher.

"Fernando, will you paint pictures on my house?" asked Señora Alfaro.

"And mine, too?" asked Señor Remon.

Fernando nodded yes, but he kept on painting.

For fun he added a black, white-faced monkey looking down at the people through purple flowers.

Next to the door he painted a big red-and-yellow rooster, flopping its red comb as it crowed a loud "cock-a-doodle-doo!"

Above the door he painted the words Casa Familia Espino, so people would know that this was the home of the Espino family.

31

Now his pictures were finished. Fernando sat down with his teacher and the neighbors. Everyone said kind words about his paintings.

Fernando said nothing. He just smiled and thought to himself, there are still six adobe houses left to paint in Sabana Grande.

Painting Mist and Fog

An Art Lesson by Molly Bang

Sometimes warm air blows over a lake or the sea or very wet land, and as it blows, it pulls the water up into itself, and the water forms millions of tiny drops of mist or fog. Then everything around us looks soft and fuzzy. Things that are far away may disappear completely from our view.

Painting pictures of mist and fog is easy. You'll need a bamboo brush, India ink, and some absorbent paper, like Manila paper or white construction paper. For this lesson, you'll also need a small jar of ink and water mixed together to form a nice medium gray.

Dip your brush into the gray until it is completely wet. Then, starting at the upper left side of your paper, slowly paint all the way across the top in a straight line. Just underneath, paint another line so the two lines blend into one. Continue doing this until your whole paper is covered with gray. Make the gray as solid and regular as you can, but if there are some streaky patches, don't worry. Mist and fog have streaky patches, too.

Painting Hills

Down at the bottom of your paper, use the black ink to paint a large hill or maybe two hills. Fill the hill in with ink all the way to the bottom of the page.

Now dip your brush into the ink and then rinse it a little in the gray, and make a hill or two hills higher up on the paper. Fill in these hills *almost* all the way down to the darker hills; leave a little space between them. Painters leave this space because our eyes make this space when we look at things. If something is dark, our eyes make a white space around it. If something is lighter than the background, our eyes make a dark line around it. In this way, our eyes help us separate the things we see from each other. When we paint, we separate things from each other by leaving a space between them.

With the ink that is still on your brush, paint one or two or three hills high up on the page.

Fill them in almost down to the second hills.

Do the mountains look as if they are disappearing into the mist? Do the high hills look as if they are far, far away?

Try making two or three pictures of hills. Turn the paper sideways, so some pictures have high hills and others have low, wide hills.

Painting Pine Trees

Cover the page with gray to make mist or fog. Let the paper dry out a little.

Now dip your brush into the gray. Halfway up the picture, paint a straight line going up a little ways—not too much, just a little. If the line isn't perfectly straight, that's fine; pine trees are seldom perfectly straight. Make some branches coming off the sides, just at the top of the tree.

Dip your brush into the ink and then rinse it a little in the gray. Starting lower down on the page, paint a line going almost to the top and then paint the branches.

Now dip your brush into the black ink and paint a larger tree, starting almost at the bottom of the page and going almost to the top, and paint the branches. If you feel like painting some more trees, remember the lighter trees should start higher up on the page so they look like they are farther away.

Painting Tree-Covered Mountains in the Mist

You can combine what you have just learned in the two pictures and make a picture of pine-covered hills disappearing into the mist. Can you do it?

Lon Po Po

A RED-RIDING HOOD STORY FROM CHINA

ED YOUNG

Once, long ago, there was a woman who lived alone in the country with her three children, Shang, Tao, and Paotze. On the day of their grandmother's birthday, the good mother set off to see her, leaving the three children at home.

Before she left, she said, "Be good while I am away, my heart-loving children; I will not return tonight. Remember to close the door tight at sunset and latch it well."

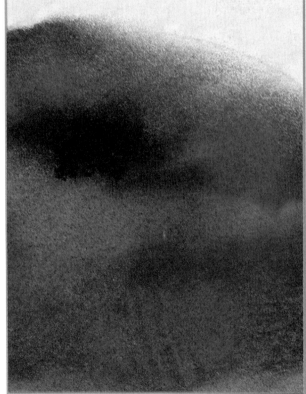

But an old wolf lived nearby and saw the good mother leave. At dusk, disguised as an old woman, he came up to the house of the children and knocked on the door twice: bang, bang.

Shang, who was the eldest, said through the latched door, "Who is it?"

"My little jewels," said the wolf, "this is your grandmother, your Po Po."

"Po Po!" Shang said. "Our mother has gone to visit you!"

The wolf acted surprised. "To visit me? I have not met her along the way. She must have taken a different route."

"Po Po!" Shang said. "How is it that you come so late?"

The wolf answered, "The journey is long, my children, and the day is short."

Shang listened through the door. "Po Po," she said, "why is your voice so low?"

"Your grandmother has caught a cold, good children, and it is dark and windy out here. Quickly open up, and let your Po Po come in," the cunning wolf said.

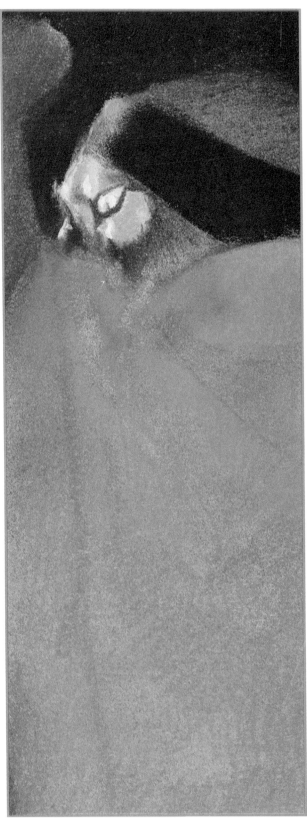

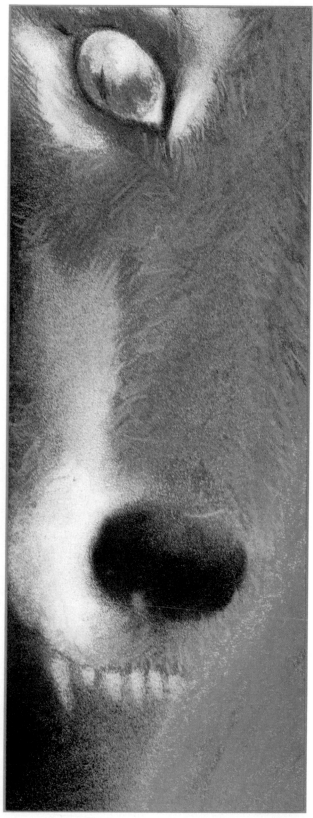

Tao and Paotze could
not wait. One unlatched the
door and the other opened it.
They shouted, "Po Po, Po Po,
come in!"

At the moment he entered
the door, the wolf blew out the
candle.

"Po Po," Shang asked, "why
did you blow out the candle?
The room is now dark."

The wolf did not answer.

Tao and Paotze rushed to
their Po Po and wished to be
hugged. The old wolf held Tao.
"Good child, you are so plump."
He embraced Paotze. "Good
child, you have grown to be
so sweet."

Soon the old wolf pretended
to be sleepy. He yawned. "All
the chicks are in the coop," he
said. "Po Po is sleepy too."

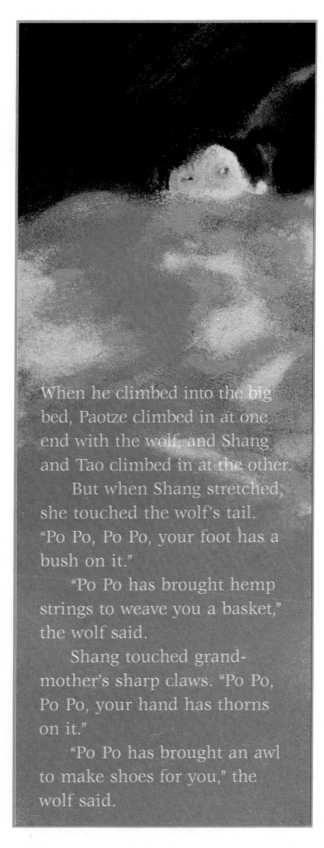

When he climbed into the big
bed, Paotze climbed in at one
end with the wolf, and Shang
and Tao climbed in at the other.

But when Shang stretched,
she touched the wolf's tail.
"Po Po, Po Po, your foot has a
bush on it."

"Po Po has brought hemp
strings to weave you a basket,"
the wolf said.

Shang touched grand-
mother's sharp claws. "Po Po,
Po Po, your hand has thorns
on it."

"Po Po has brought an awl
to make shoes for you," the
wolf said.

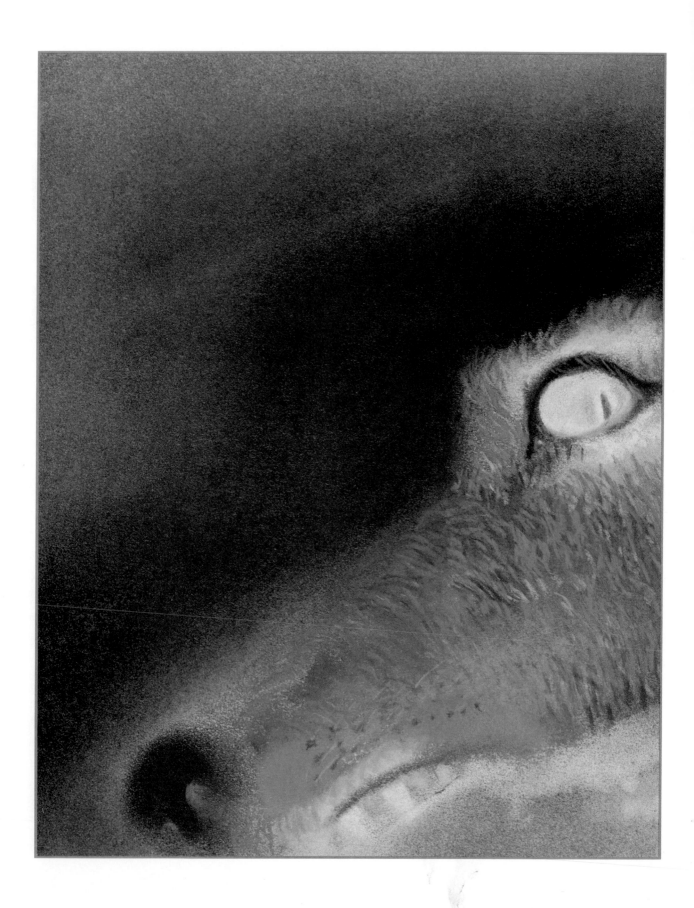

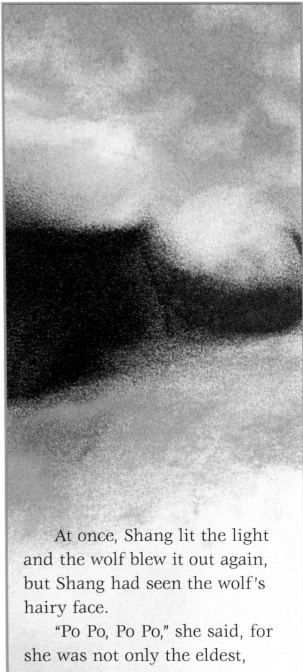

At once, Shang lit the light
and the wolf blew it out again,
but Shang had seen the wolf's
hairy face.

"Po Po, Po Po," she said, for
she was not only the eldest,
she was the most clever, "you
must be hungry. Have you
eaten gingko nuts?"

"What is gingko?" the wolf
asked.

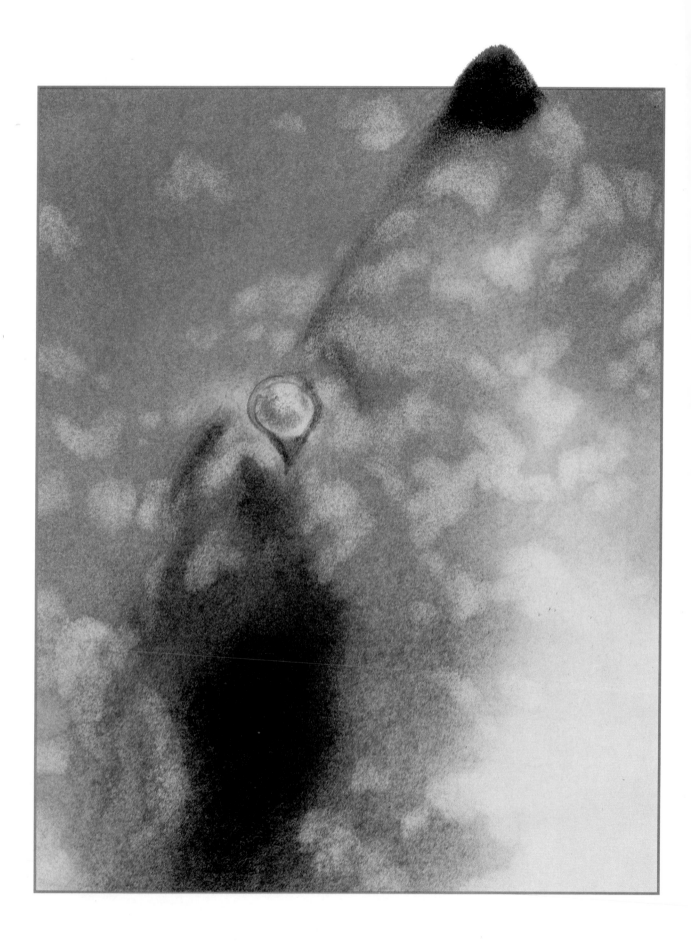

"Gingko is soft and tender, like the skin of a baby. One taste and you will live forever," Shang said, "and the nuts grow on the top of the tree just outside the door."

The wolf gave a sigh. "Oh, dear. Po Po is old, her bones have become brittle. No longer can she climb trees."

"Good Po Po, we can pick some for you," Shang said.

The wolf was delighted.

Shang jumped out of bed and Tao and Paotze came with her to the gingko tree. There, Shang told her sisters about the wolf and all three climbed up the tall tree.

The wolf waited and waited. Plump Tao did not come back. Sweet Paotze did not come back. Shang did not come back, and no one brought any nuts from the gingko tree. At last the wolf shouted, "Where are you, children?"

"Po Po," Shang called out, "we are on the top of the tree eating gingko nuts."

50

"Good children," the wolf begged, "pluck some for me."

"But Po Po, gingko is magic only when it is plucked directly from the tree. You must come and pluck it from the tree yourself."

The wolf came outside and paced back and forth under the tree where he heard the three children eating the gingko nuts at the top. "Oh, Po Po, these nuts are so tasty! The skin so tender," Shang said. The wolf's mouth began to water for a taste.

Finally, Shang, the eldest and most clever child, said, "Po Po, Po Po, I have a plan. At the door there is a big basket. Behind it is a rope. Tie the rope to the basket, sit in the basket and throw the other end to me. I can pull you up."

The wolf was overjoyed and fetched the basket and the rope, then threw one end of the rope to the top of the tree. Shang caught the rope and began to pull the basket up and up.

Halfway she let go of the rope, and the basket and the wolf fell to the ground.

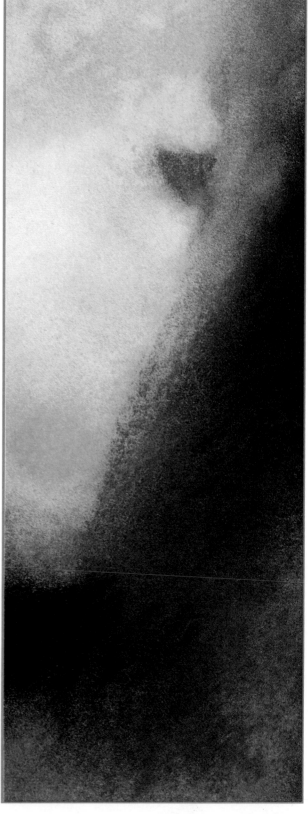

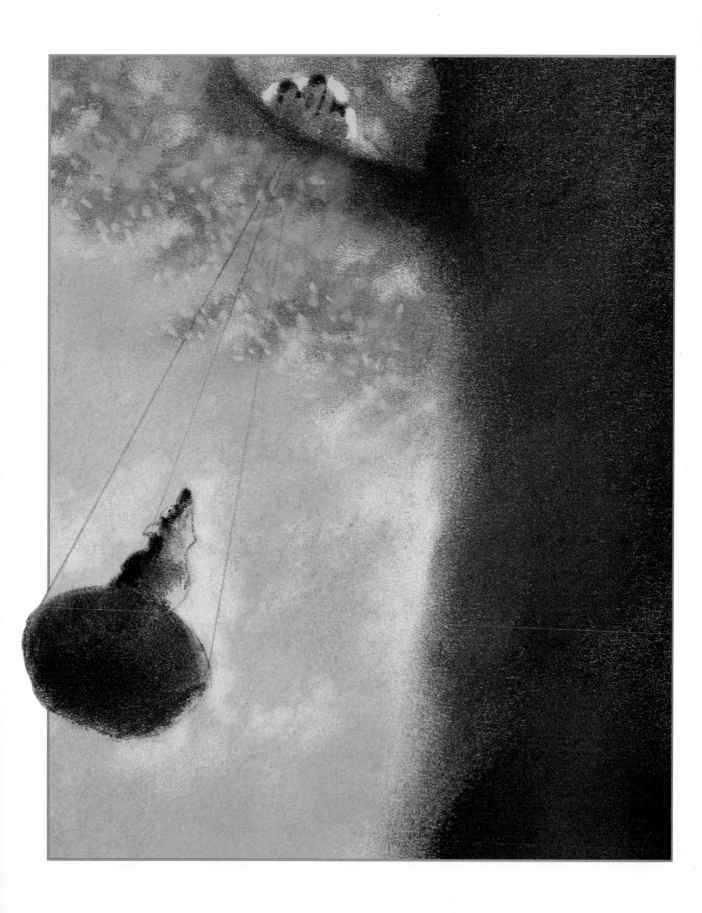

"I am so small and weak, Po Po," Shang pretended. "I could not hold the rope alone."

"This time I will help," Tao said. "Let us do it again."

The wolf had only one thought in his mind: to taste a gingko nut. He climbed into the basket again. Now Shang and Tao pulled the rope on the basket together, higher and higher.

Again, they let go, and again the wolf tumbled down, down, and bumped his head.

The wolf was furious. He growled and cursed. "We could not hold the rope, Po Po," Shang said, "but only one gingko nut and you will be well again."

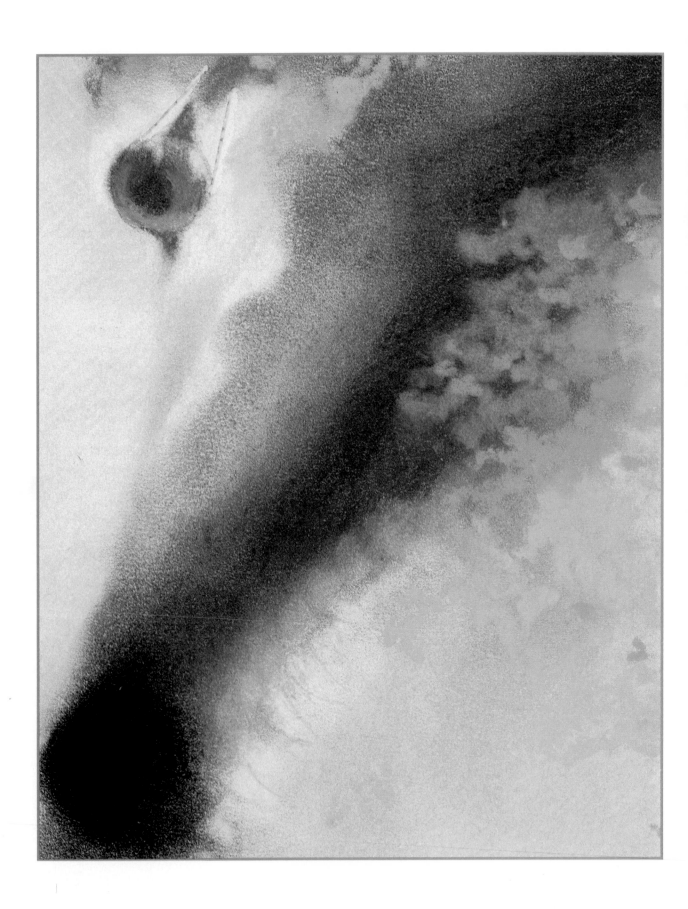

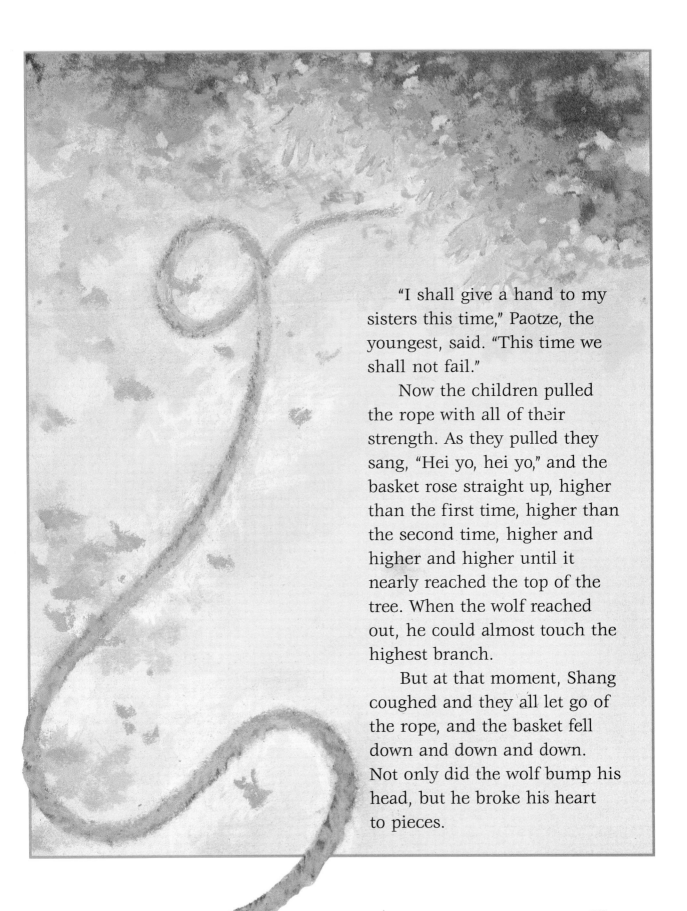

"I shall give a hand to my sisters this time," Paotze, the youngest, said. "This time we shall not fail."

Now the children pulled the rope with all of their strength. As they pulled they sang, "Hei yo, hei yo," and the basket rose straight up, higher than the first time, higher than the second time, higher and higher and higher until it nearly reached the top of the tree. When the wolf reached out, he could almost touch the highest branch.

But at that moment, Shang coughed and they all let go of the rope, and the basket fell down and down and down. Not only did the wolf bump his head, but he broke his heart to pieces.

"Po Po," Shang shouted, but there was no answer.

"Po Po," Tao shouted, but there was no answer.

"Po Po," Paotze shouted. There was still no answer. The children climbed to the branches just above the wolf and saw that he was truly dead. Then they climbed down, went into the house, closed the door, locked the door with the latch and fell peacefully asleep.

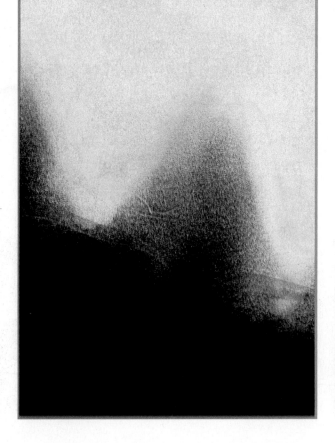

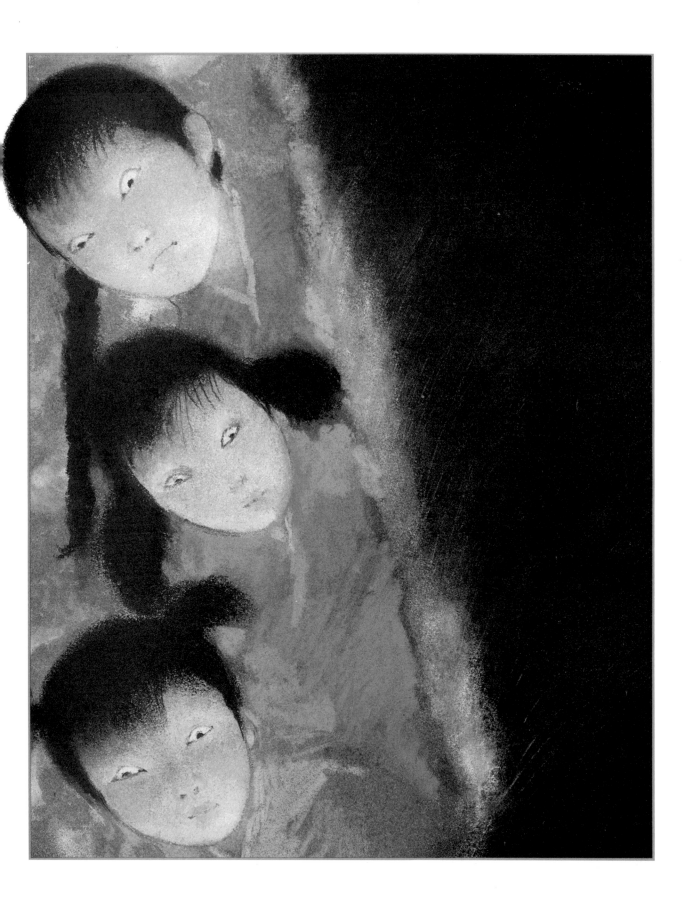

On the next day, their
mother returned with baskets
of food from their real Po Po,
and the three sisters told her
the story of the Po Po who
had come.

MEET

Ed Young

While growing up in China, Ed Young loved to hear old Chinese folk tales. One favorite was the tale of Lon Po Po. As he listened, he never imagined that someday he would write the tale in English, add his own drawings, and win the Caldecott Medal.

Young remembers that he nearly always had a pencil in his hand when he was a boy. "I drew everything that happened to cross my mind: airplanes, people, a tall ship that my father was very proud of, a hunter and a bird dog that came out of my head." He kept on drawing when he moved to New York City and got a job. During his lunch hours, he sat in Central Park Zoo and drew animals.

One day Young was told to see an editor at a large publishing company. He carried a shopping bag containing animal drawings. The editor liked his work and asked him to do the drawings for *The Mean Mouse and Other Mean Stories*.

Since then, Young has drawn pictures for over fifty books, five of which he wrote himself.

Tinkering

I love beginning with
a clean sheet and
laying down each grease-black
cog and bolt and link
aligning positions
adjusting tensions and
checking for wear.

I love finishing in
reverse order and
picking up each clean, oiled
sprocket, nut and washer
spinning the wheel
and hearing only the whirr
of everything in place.

Diane Dawber

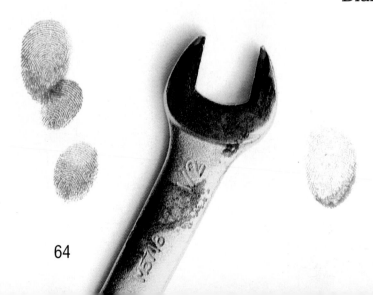

The Painter as Musician and Magician,
a sculpture made from bicycle parts,
cardboard, and found objects, by
Bruno Pasquier-Desvignes.

ANIMAL FACT/
Animal Fable

by Seymour Simon

Illustrated by Diane de Groat

We all know *facts* about animals—things that are true. But from watching animals and reading stories and tales about them, we may have some beliefs that are not true. We may believe in *fables* rather than facts.

In this science selection, decide whether each statement about an animal is a fact or a fable. Then turn the page to find out what scientists have discovered.

A turtle can walk out of its shell.

Fable When people find an empty turtle shell on the ground, they may think a turtle left it behind and moved into a new one. But that is not true. A turtle can no more walk out of its shell than you can walk away from your ribs.

A turtle's shell is not just a house it lives in. The shell is really part of the turtle's body. You should not try to take a turtle out of its shell. If you do, the turtle will die. The empty shells you may find on the ground are the remains of turtles that have died.

Crickets tell the temperature with their chirps.

FACT Crickets are animals whose body temperatures change with the temperature around them. On a hot day, crickets chirp so rapidly that it is hard to count the number of chirps. But on a cool day, crickets chirp much more slowly. We can then easily count the times they chirp.

Some people say they can use the number of chirps to find the exact temperature. That's not always possible. A cricket's chirping depends upon its age and health as well as on the temperature.

Porcupines shoot their quills.

Fable   Porcupines cannot really shoot their quills. A porcupine's quills are sharp and have barbs like tiny hooks. The tip of a quill shown here has been magnified many times. When the quill sinks into an animal it becomes stuck and is left behind.

Porcupines use their quills to protect themselves. If an animal or person bothers a porcupine, the quills stand on end. The porcupine turns around and backs up to his enemy. Few animals bother a porcupine a second time.

Dogs talk with their tails.

FACT We know dogs don't use words to talk, but their tails can tell us how they feel. When a dog wags its tail from side to side, the dog is happy and playful. But when a dog wags its tail up and down, it may be because it has done something wrong and expects to be punished.

If a dog keeps its tail straight up, be careful. That is the signal that it may attack. Don't run, just back away slowly.

Ostriches hide their heads in the sand.

Fable There is a well-known fable that ostriches stick their heads in the sand when they are frightened. Here's how the fable may have started. When ostriches see an enemy, they sometimes drop down and stretch out their necks along the ground. This makes it more difficult for the enemy to see them. To a person watching an ostrich, it may look as if the ostrich has buried its head in the ground.

An ostrich may not be very smart, but it is not dumb. When an enemy comes close, the ostrich gets up from the ground and runs away.

Goats will eat almost anything.

FACT Goats will eat almost anything they can find. They even seem to eat tin cans. But they are not really eating the metal can; they are chewing the label to get at the glue underneath.

Though goats eat string and paper, they would rather eat fruit, vegetables, grass, and leaves of plants. They are not quite the "garbage cans" some people think they are.

MEET
SEYMOUR SIMON

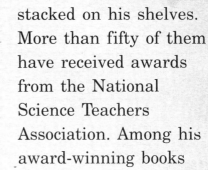

Are you full of questions about the world? Do you wonder why fall weather turns some leaves red and others yellow? Is it a puzzle to you how a heavy ship can float? Science writer Seymour Simon likes questions like these. He says, "It's questions . . . that occur to me and that have been asked of me by children . . . that make me want to write science books."

Simon was a science teacher for twenty-three years. (He must have answered a million questions during those years!) Now he writes books full-time. Nearly 150 books with his name on the front are stacked on his shelves. More than fifty of them have received awards from the National Science Teachers Association. Among his award-winning books are *Mirror Magic, Stars,* and *The Moon.*

To answer questions for his books, Simon says he has "collected rocks, dug under rotting logs, tramped through swamps." He has also shared his home with earthworms, gerbils, ants, and crickets. He says about his books, "Sometimes I'll provide an answer, but more often I'll suggest an activity or an experiment that will let a child answer a question by trying it out."

BOOK REVIEWS

Title: **Animal Fact/Animal Fable**
Author: **Seymour Simon**
Illustrator: **Diane de Groat**

Reviewed by:
Matthew Cella

The book is about animal facts, or things that are true. It also includes animal fables, which are things that are not true about animals.

I was surprised to learn that ostriches don't bury their heads in the sand. This is a fable. I also thought porcupines shoot their quills. This is a fable, too.

I liked the way this book was set up. It gave information on the first page. You had to guess if it was true or not. On the second page, it told you. I got some right and a few wrong.

I would recommend this book. I like Seymour Simon's books. Saturn was another book of his that I read. I also liked Diane de Groat's illustrations.

Matthew Cella

Michael T. Smalls

This book is about what some animals do and what they don't do. Real facts and fables!

Some surprising information was that turtles cannot come out of their shell because it is a part of their body. Crickets tell the temperature by their chirps, and a porcupine quill has a sharp barb that can stick you if you get too close, but they don't shoot quills. I learned that if a dog's tail is straight up it may attack you!

I liked the way the information was set up—a statement and the next page gave you the answer, I liked that! I would recommend this book to a friend. I have not read other books by Mr. Simon, but I would like to.

Michael Smalls

Christina Marie Cesar

The new thing I learned was that a dog can talk with its tail. If a dog wags its tail side to side it means that it is happy and playful. If a dog wags its tail up and down it means it knows it did something bad and expects to be punished. If the dog's tail is straight up, watch out. It may attack you. Walk away slowly.

The thing I found most interesting was that goats eat mostly anything. They eat tin cans. They don't really eat the metal, they just chew the label to get to the glue underneath.

Christina Cesar

How Come? And

What If?

The world is so full of astonishing things:

Spider spun silk, butterfly wings,

Pink petal puffs on an apricot tree,

Spirally shells that sing of the sea,

Quick swishy fishes,

and creatures that crawl,

Enormously big or amazingly small.

With all of these things to delight us about,

There are thousands of questions to wonder about.

How come? And what if?

And suppose this were so?

It's exciting to wonder about what we know.

Joy Hulme

Thinking

Silently
Inside my head
Behind my eyes
A thought begins to grow and be
A part of me.
And then I think
I always knew
The thing I only got to know,
As though it always
Was right there
Inside my head
Behind my eyes
Where I keep things.

Felice Holman

MEET AN Underwater EXPLORER

Sylvia studies ocean life
right where it's happening!

by Luise Woelflein

Sylvia Earle has spent more
than 6000 hours under water.
She has played around with
friendly dolphins. She has
gotten "personal" with animals
that can be dangerous, such as
sharks and moray eels. She has
studied humpback whales by
following them under water.

Once a deadly poisonous
lionfish stung her. It took Sylvia
an hour to get to the surface of
the water, where she could get
help. Another time, a shark was
threatening to bite her. She
kicked it, and luckily it swam
away.

She flips for science! Sylvia dives into a giant basket sponge just to see what's inside. The scientist has spent more than 6000 hours under water studying ocean plants and animals.

Sylvia is a *marine biologist*—a scientist who studies ocean life. She's also one of the world's best underwater divers. And as an ocean scientist, she has done lots of firsts:

- She set new diving records and tested new equipment.
- She was the first woman to become the chief scientist for an important government group in Washington, D.C.
- She was the head of an all-woman science team that *lived* on the floor of the Atlantic Ocean for two weeks. There, she found 153 species (kinds) of plants—including 26 species that had never been seen in that area before.

Being an ocean scientist and an underwater diver fit right together. Sylvia can study life in the ocean—as it's happening.

FROM THE BEGINNING

Ever since she was a little girl, Sylvia has looked for ways to get under water. On family vacations at the New Jersey Shore, she learned the basics—how to swim past the waves and into deeper water. Then, when she was 12, her family moved to Florida.

Sylvia spent hundreds of hours playing there in the warm, clear waters of the Gulf of Mexico. "Wearing a mask, I would float for hours facedown on an inner tube, just watching," she says.

When Sylvia got to college, she tried out scuba gear for the first time. (Scuba gear is equipment for breathing under water.) "It was glorious!" she says. "It was like being a fish. My professor almost had to haul me out of the water by force, I liked it so much."

It's still hard to get Sylvia out of the water. In fact, she wants lots of people to learn how to explore the ocean. Why? Because so little is known about what's there.

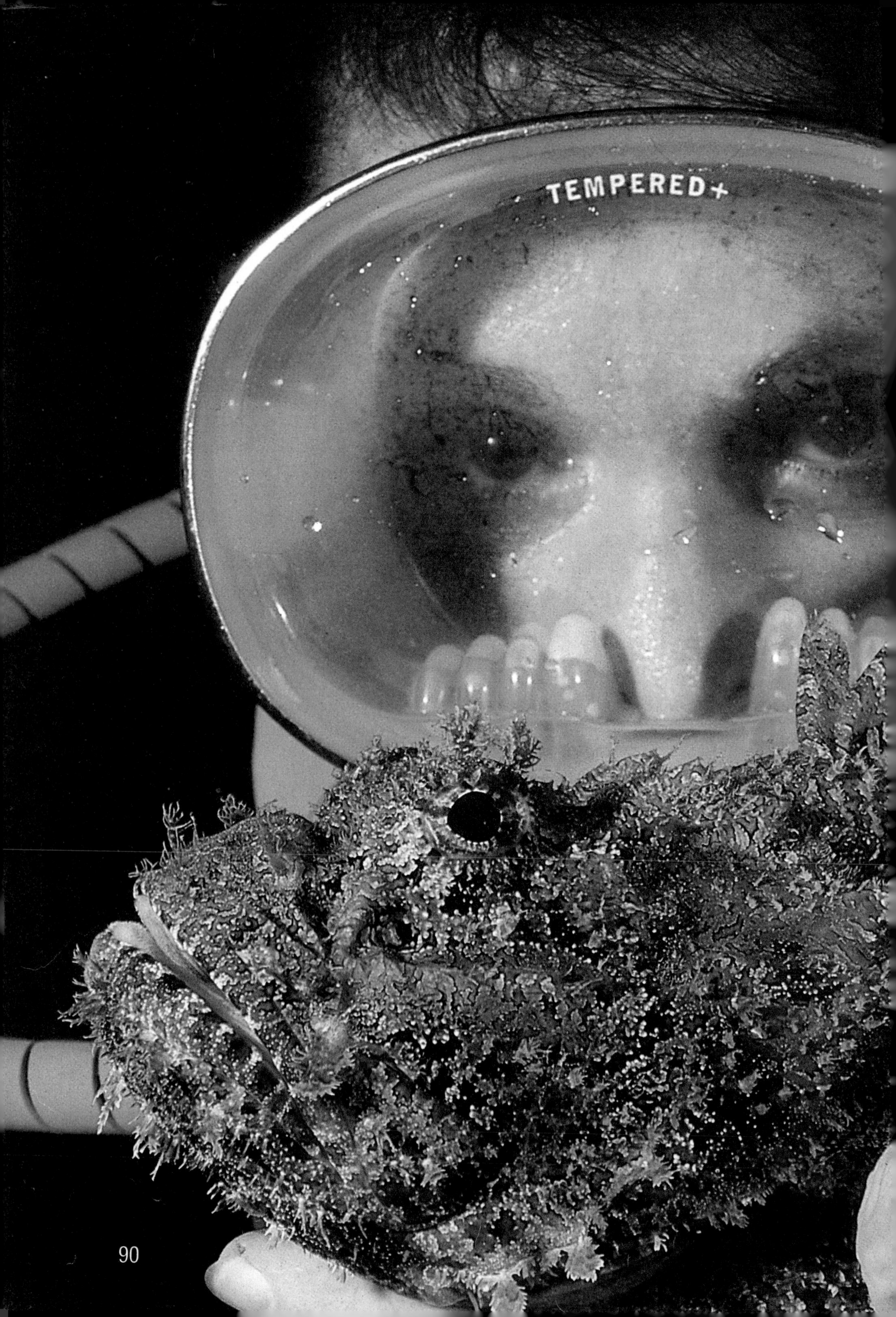
TEMPERED

Neat rock, huh? Actually, this "rock" is a scorpionfish. Look out—those sharp spines on its back are full of *poison!* So why in the world is this woman holding the creature? To study it!

WHAT **IS** DOWN THERE?

Sylvia points out that more than two-thirds of our planet is covered with water. But less than 10 percent of the ocean has been explored.

Most of what we know about the ocean comes from studying the things we've taken out of it with hooks and nets. Imagine exploring your neighborhood by blindfolding yourself and dipping nets from a helicopter! That's kind of how people have been exploring the ocean.

Until recently, very few people were able to go on long, deep dives. Why? Two big problems had to be overcome. You can probably guess the first—people can't breathe under water. But now there's equipment such as scuba gear that divers can use for breathing.

The other big problem is *pressure.* You probably know that water weighs a lot. (If you don't believe it, try picking up a bucketful sometime!)

When you dive down deep, a great amount of weight pushes on your body from all sides. And the deeper you go, the worse it gets. It can even crush your body if you dive too deep. To overcome this, people have invented suits and vehicles that can stand the pressure.

Sylvia was the first person to try out some of these inventions. In one of them, she set a record. She made the deepest dive in a suit that wasn't connected to a boat at the surface.

Sylvia is always trying to find ways to go deeper into the ocean. The machine—Deep Flight (left)—may be able to take her down to 4000 feet (1200 m) when it's finished. Don't worry—her dog, Blue, won't be going with her.

Dinner down under: Sylvia led this team of scientists called Tektite 2. (Sylvia is in the blue shirt.) The team spent two weeks living in a kind of "underwater hotel" and studying the ocean life around them.

INTO THE DEEP

Sylvia made that record-breaking dive off the coast of Hawaii. She was wearing a Jim Suit (named for a British diver named Jim Jarrett). It looks a bit like a space suit.

After Sylvia got into the suit, divers attached her to the front of a tiny submarine. The sub and Sylvia went down together.

She watched as the bright water at the surface slowly grew darker. The sub went down, down, down. It finally landed on the ocean floor in inky-black water 1250 feet (375 m) deep.

At Sylvia's signal, one of the people in the sub released the safety belt that was holding Sylvia in place. She stepped away from the sub and onto the ocean floor.

For 2 1/2 hours, Sylvia walked on the bottom of the Pacific Ocean. The sub followed her around, shining lights so she could see. So much was going on! A green-eyed shark swam by. Sylvia also saw strange eels, crabs, and glowing lantern fish.

Look—an underwater astronaut! Sylvia set a diving record wearing this Jim Suit. Above, she took a practice run in shallow water to get used to the suit. Then on the big day (left), she dived 1250 feet (375 m). That was the deepest dive anyone had ever made in a suit that wasn't connected to a boat at the surface.

Sylvia plays with a dolphin she calls Sandy. The scientist says she learns most about ocean animals by going where they live.

GOING DEEPER

Walking on the bottom of the ocean in a Jim Suit was exciting. But it was a slow and clunky way to get around.

That's how it is for people using Jim Suits and scuba gear. They can travel only as fast as they can walk or swim. So they can't keep up with dolphins, whales, or many other ocean animals they want to study.

Sylvia dreams of being able to dive to the deepest part of the ocean and "fly" through the sea as fast as a fish. And she's working on making that dream come true.

She and an engineer friend, Graham Hawkes, have made new one-person subs. Both Sylvia and Graham have used them to dive to 3000 feet (900 m) —deeper than anyone has ever traveled alone before. Another sub, called Deep Flight, should be able to take a person to the deepest part of the ocean and back. Sylvia can't wait to use it!

TROUBLED WATERS

During her lifetime, Sylvia has seen a lot of sad changes take place in the sea she loves. The clear Florida waters she used to explore as a child are now cloudy. Many sea creatures all over the world are endangered because of overfishing, pollution, and other people-caused problems.

Sylvia thinks that by harming the ocean, people may harm themselves. "Everything on Earth works together," she says. Tiny plants in the ocean make a lot of oxygen. If we destroy those plants, Sylvia believes, we destroy a big source of the oxygen we need to breathe. Changing the ocean may make other changes as well. In fact, she believes it may even change the Earth's weather.

"Besides," Sylvia says, "sea creatures are beautiful and precious, and they deserve to be protected just for that reason."

MANY MYSTERIES

Sylvia wishes that everyone could go under water and see the ocean as she does. Then they might better understand the importance of saving it.

Sylvia also hopes that more people will explore the ocean. "We know so little about how the ocean works," she says. "And we have no idea how many strange, new kinds of plants and animals are waiting to be discovered there.

"Some lucky kids will have the pleasure of solving these mysteries when they grow up," she says.

Sylvia, too, continues to explore and discover. There's still so much she wants to know and see. And she's willing to go to great *depths* to do it!

Sylvia collects tiny plants called algae near a Pacific Ocean island. She likes looking for new plants. And scientists have named many newly found plants after Sylvia.

MEET
LUISE WOELFLEIN

Growing up on a farm in Pennsylvania, Luise Woelflein loved to explore nature. Even today, her favorite times are spent exploring nature's mysteries. Forests, mountains, seas, and even swamps are all places of wonder for her.

When not outdoors, Luise is busy writing. Her science books for children combine two loves—nature and writing. Among her books are *Forest Animals* and *The Ultimate Bug Book*. She has also written lessons to help teachers make science fun for students. As Luise explains, "From bears to bugs and trees to turtles, I like writing about nature to help people understand the weird and wonderful world we live in."

Nathaniel's

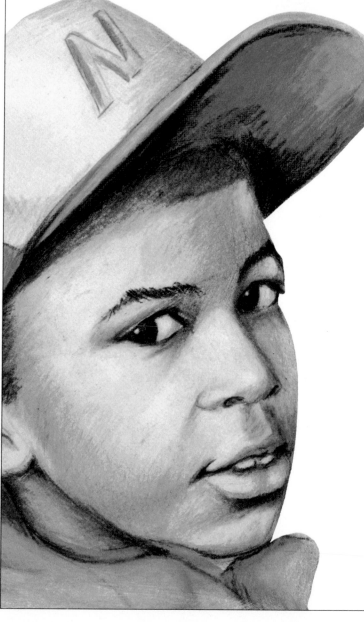

It's Nathaniel talking
and Nathaniel's me
I'm talking about
My philosophy
About the things I do
And the people I see
All told in the words
Of Nathaniel B. Free
That's me
And I can rap
I can rap
I can rap, rap, rap
Till your earflaps flap
I can talk that talk
Till you go for a walk
I can run it on down
Till you get out of town
I can rap

Rap

I can rap
Rested, dressed and feeling fine
I've got something on my mind
Friends and kin and neighborhood
Listen now and listen good
Nathaniel's talking
Nathaniel B. Free
Talking about
My philosophy
Been thinking all day
I got a lot to say
Gotta run it on down
Nathaniel's way
Okay!
I gotta rap
Gotta rap
Gotta rap, rap, rap
Till your earflaps flap

Gotta talk that talk
Till you go for a walk
Gotta run it on down
Till you get out of town
Gotta rap
Gotta rap
Rested, dressed and feeling fine
I've got something on my mind
Friends and kin and neighborhood
Listen now and listen good
I'm gonna rap, hey!
Gonna rap, hey!
Gonna rap, hey!
I'm gonna rap!

Eloise Greenfield

Unit 2

See for Yourself

The Terrible EEK

A Japanese Tale

Retold by Patricia A. Compton

Illustrated by Sheila Hamanaka

A long time ago, in a certain place in the mountains, it began to rain. The wind shook a small house with a thatch roof.

Inside, a boy and his father sat warming their hands over a small fire. Nearby, the boy's mother prepared the evening meal.

The sounds of the wind and rain battering at the house frightened the little boy. "Father, are you ever afraid?" the boy asked.

"Yes, my son, there are things that I fear," the father answered.

"What do you fear most?" the boy asked.

"Among humans," the father replied, "I am most afraid of a thief."

It happened that a thief had climbed on to the thatch roof of the house and was hiding up there. When the thief heard the father's reply, he was triumphant. "I am the strongest and most fearsome of creatures," he said to himself. "I am what they are most afraid of."

"Among animals," the father continued, "I am most afraid of the wolf."

At that very moment, a wolf was sneaking by the side of the house with plans to steal a chicken or two for his dinner.

The wolf sniffed haughtily and said to himself, "I am the strongest and most fearsome of creatures. I am what they are most afraid of."

"But the most frightening thing of all to me," the father went on telling his son, "is a terrible leak. I hope there are no leaks tonight."

The wolf stopped a moment and thought, "What is a terrible leak?" He had never heard of a terrible leak. It must be an awful creature if they are most afraid of it.

A noisy gust of wind blew away some of the sounds of the father's words before they reached the thief on the roof. All he heard was ". . . the most frightening thing of all is a terrible eek."

The thief wondered what a terrible eek could be. He reached up to scratch his head and lost his balance. Then he slipped on the wet thatch and slid off the roof, landing right on the back of the wolf.

Now the poor thief thought he had landed on the back of the terrible eek. And the wolf thought that the terrible leak had landed on him.

The wolf howled, then ran with all his might toward the woods. He was hoping the terrible leak would fall off. The thief clutched the wolf's neck and hung on with all his might.

As they sped through the forest, the thief saw a low-hanging branch.

In one quick motion, he let go of the wolf's neck, grabbed the branch, and swung free.

The thief was so relieved to be away from the terrible eek that he did not notice that the branch was too weak to hold him. It cracked and he fell.

It happened that there was a deep hole right under the tree. The thief tumbled into the hole and could not climb up the steep, slippery sides.

The wolf, feeling the weight leave his back, ran to his den. Once there he collapsed, completely out of breath. After the wolf finally caught his breath, he felt very thirsty. He peered cautiously out of his den. Not seeing anything, he went to the water hole for a drink. There he met a tiger.

"Tiger, do you know what a terrible leak is?" asked the wolf. "Humans fear it more than anything. It jumped on my back and nearly choked me to death. Will you help me catch the leak?"

"I have never heard of a terrible leak. I thought I was the strongest and most frightening creature in the world," the tiger said. "Yes, I will go with you to catch the terrible leak."

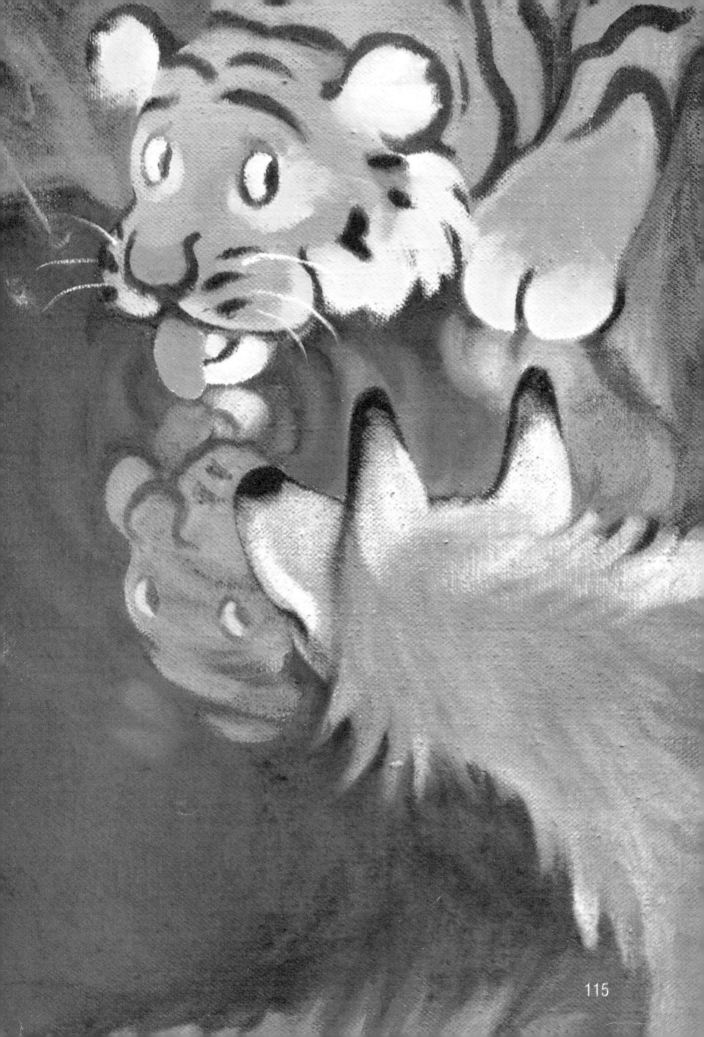

A monkey sitting in a nearby tree heard the tiger and the wolf talking. "Where are you going?" he asked.

"We are going to catch the terrible leak," said the tiger. "Will you come along and help us?"

"I have never heard of a terrible leak, and I am not strong and frightening like you are," said the monkey, "but I am clever. So I will come and help you catch it."

The tiger and the monkey followed the wolf back to the tree where the terrible leak had jumped off the wolf's back.

The monkey found the big hole under the tree and said, "I will put my tail down into the hole and see if the leak tries to grab it."

"Are you there, terrible leak?" cried the monkey, lowering his tail into the hole.

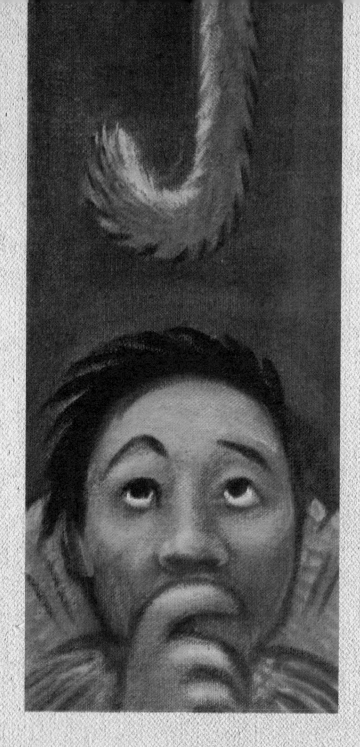

When the thief saw the
monkey's tail, he grabbed tight
and pulled.

The monkey became very
frightened, and he pulled with all
his might. The monkey pulled the
thief right out of the hole.

119

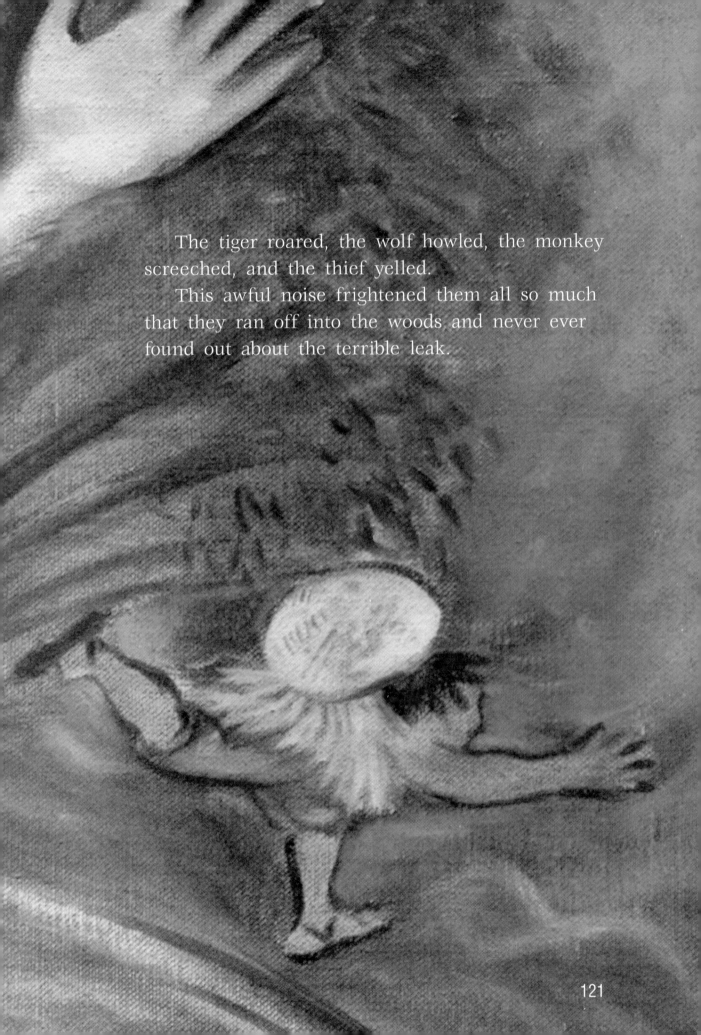

The tiger roared, the wolf howled, the monkey screeched, and the thief yelled.

This awful noise frightened them all so much that they ran off into the woods and never ever found out about the terrible leak.

After a while, the rain stopped and the moon came out and shone on the little house with the thatch roof.

The boy and his mother and father were sound asleep in their dry, warm beds.

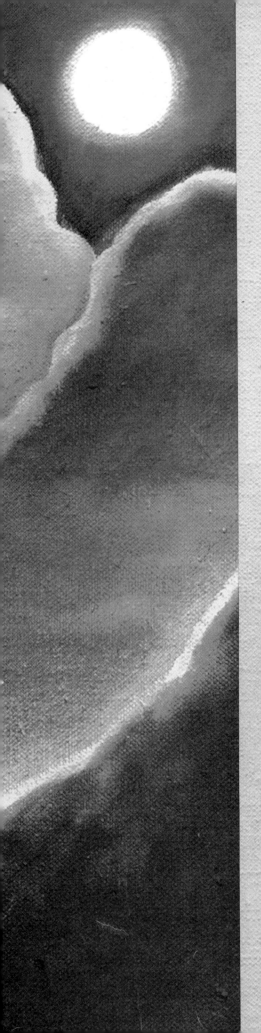

Meet
Patricia A. Compton

Patricia Compton starts with an idea of a story she wants to tell. She likes to sketch, rather than write, her ideas. Compton says, "The words come after the pictures. Then the story changes over time as I get a feel for the characters and where they lead me."

Meet
Sheila Hamanaka

A third-generation Japanese American, Sheila Hamanaka is proud of her heritage. Much of her work is based on Japanese themes and art.

Hamanaka especially enjoys drawing people and animals. She says, "I always try to draw different types of people—all ages, colors, sizes, girls and boys—because we live in a multicultural world."

123

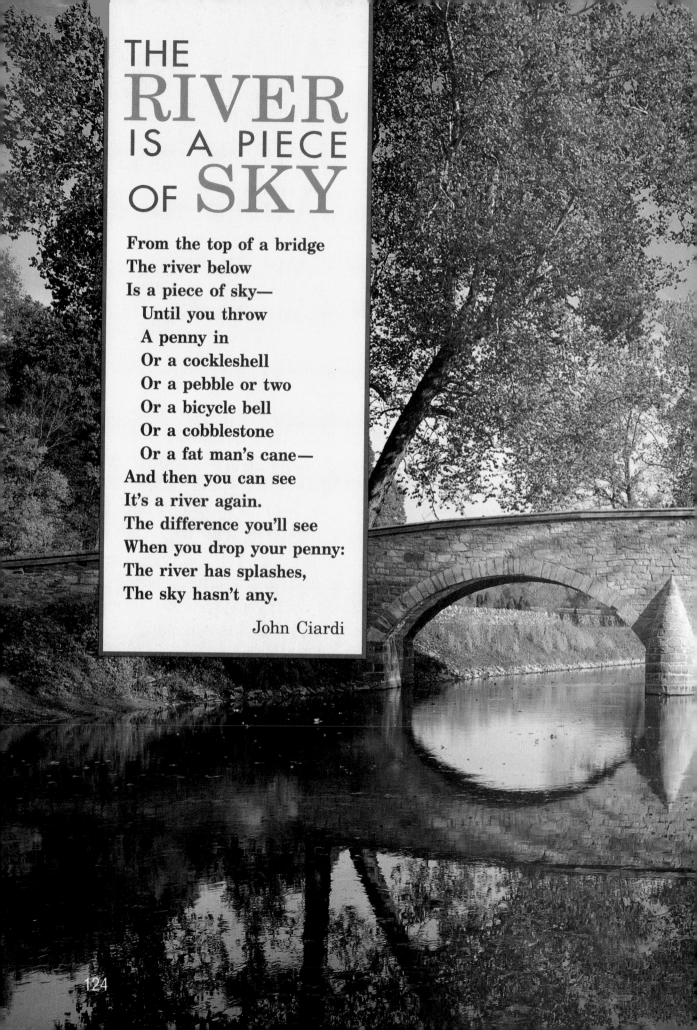

THE RIVER IS A PIECE OF SKY

From the top of a bridge
The river below
Is a piece of sky—
    Until you throw
    A penny in
    Or a cockleshell
    Or a pebble or two
    Or a bicycle bell
    Or a cobblestone
    Or a fat man's cane—
And then you can see
It's a river again.
The difference you'll see
When you drop your penny:
The river has splashes,
The sky hasn't any.

John Ciardi

124

MEET *Chris Van Allsburg*

If you saw ants in your kitchen, what would you think? If you are like a lot of people, you might think "How disgusting!" or "How interesting!" or "How cute!" However, when Chris Van Allsburg saw two ants in his kitchen, he thought: "If I were an ant looking out from an electrical socket, the long slits in which the light poured in would look like 15-foot doorways hung in space." That thought gave Chris Van Allsburg the idea for *Two Bad Ants.*

Chris Van Allsburg, with some of the sculptures he has created

Chris Van Allsburg's talent for looking at the world in unusual ways has won him the highest award for children's picture books in the United States—the Caldecott Medal. He won it not just once, but twice: for *Jumanji* in 1982 and for *The Polar Express* in 1986.

Van Allsburg's way of looking at the world has also won him many fans. One fan wrote: "I love the books you write. I am so glad you are weird because I am very weird. I think you are weird but great."

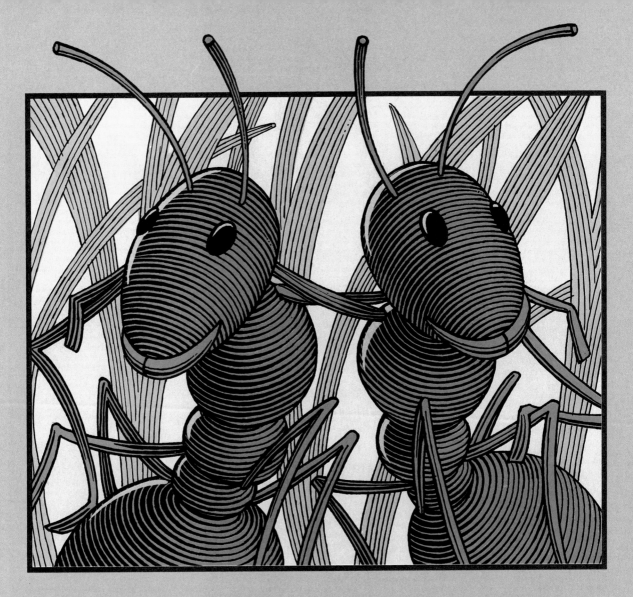

TWO
BAD
ANTS

CHRIS VAN ALLSBURG

The news traveled swiftly through the tunnels
of the ant world. A scout had returned with a
remarkable discovery—a beautiful sparkling
crystal. When the scout presented the crystal to
the ant queen she took a small bite, then quickly
ate the entire thing.

She deemed it the most delicious food she had ever tasted. Nothing could make her happier than to have more, much more. The ants understood. They were eager to gather more crystals because the queen was the mother of them all. Her happiness made the whole ant nest a happy place.

It was late in the day when they departed. Long shadows stretched over the entrance to the ant kingdom. One by one the insects climbed out, following the scout, who had made it clear—there were many crystals where the first had been found, but the journey was long and dangerous.

They marched into the woods that surrounded their underground home. Dusk turned to twilight, twilight to night. The path they followed twisted and turned, every bend leading them deeper into the dark forest.

More than once the line of ants stopped and anxiously listened for the sounds of hungry spiders. But all they heard was the call of crickets echoing through the woods like distant thunder.

Dew formed on the leaves above. Without warning, huge cold drops fell on the marching ants. A firefly passed overhead that, for an instant, lit up the woods with a blinding flash of blue-green light.

At the edge of the forest stood a mountain. The ants looked up and could not see its peak. It seemed to reach right to the heavens. But they did not stop. Up the side they climbed, higher and higher.

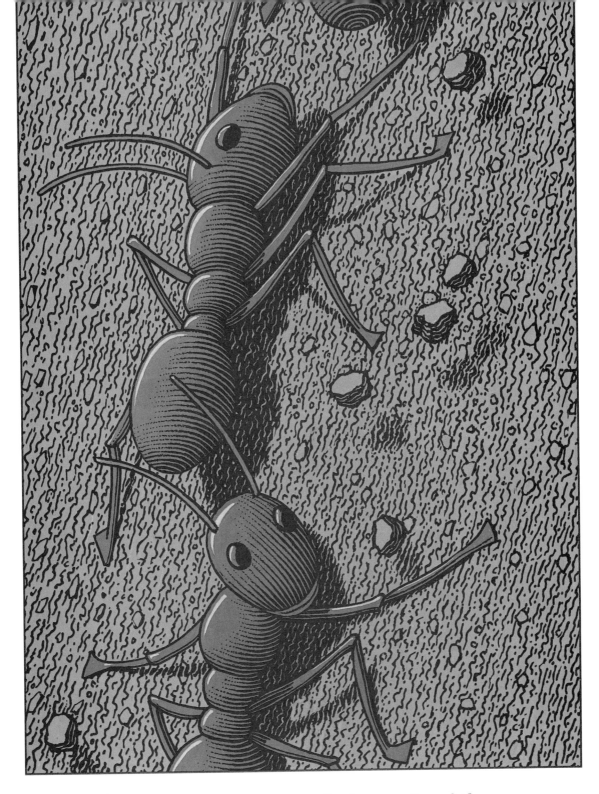

The wind whistled through the cracks of the
mountain's face. The ants could feel its force bending
their delicate antennae. Their legs grew weak as
they struggled upward. At last they reached a ledge
and crawled through a narrow tunnel.

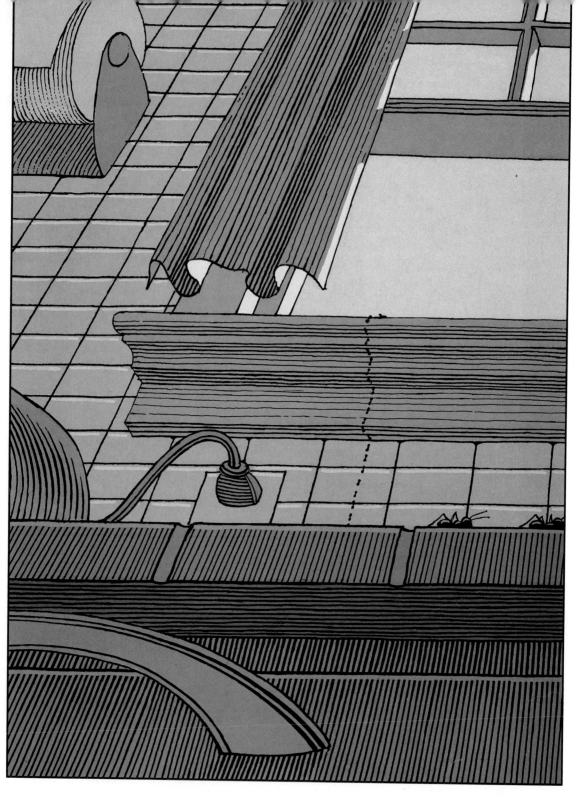

When the ants came out of the tunnel they found themselves in a strange world. Smells they had known all their lives, smells of dirt and grass and rotting plants, had vanished. There was no more wind and, most puzzling of all, it seemed that the sky was gone.

They crossed smooth shiny surfaces, then followed the scout up a glassy, curved wall. They had reached their goal. From the top of the wall they looked below to a sea of crystals. One by one the ants climbed down into the sparkling treasure.

Quickly they each chose a crystal, then turned to start the journey home. There was something about this unnatural place that made the ants nervous. In fact they left in such a hurry that none of them noticed the two small ants who stayed behind.

"Why go back?" one asked the other. "This place may not feel like home, but look at all these crystals." "You're right," said the other, "we can stay here and eat this tasty treasure every day, forever." So the two ants ate crystal after crystal until they were too full to move, and fell asleep.

Daylight came. The sleeping ants were unaware of changes taking place in their new found home. A giant silver scoop hovered above them, then plunged deep into the crystals. It shoveled up both ants and crystals and carried them high into the air.

The ants were wide awake when the scoop turned, dropping them from a frightening height. They tumbled through space in a shower of crystals and fell into a boiling brown lake.

Then the giant scoop stirred violently back and forth. Crushing waves fell over the ants. They paddled hard to keep their tiny heads above water. But the scoop kept spinning the hot brown liquid.

Around and around it went, creating a whirlpool that sucked the ants deeper and deeper. They both held their breath and finally bobbed to the surface, gasping for air and spitting mouthfuls of the terrible, bitter water.

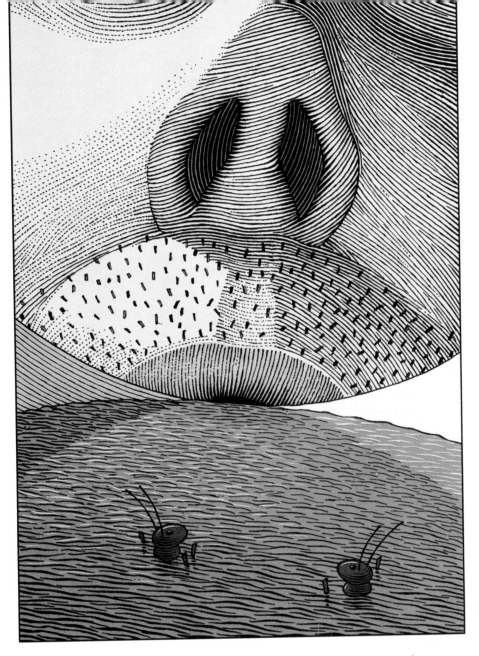

Then the lake tilted and began to empty into a cave. The ants could hear the rushing water and felt themselves pulled toward the pitch black hole. Suddenly the cave disappeared and the lake became calm. The ants swam to the shore and found that the lake had steep sides.

They hurried down the walls that held back the lake. The frightened insects looked for a place to hide, worried that the giant scoop might shovel them up again. Close by they found a huge round disk with holes that could neatly hide them.

But as soon as they had climbed inside, their hiding place was lifted, tilted, and lowered into a dark space. When the ants climbed out of the holes they were surrounded by a strange red glow. It seemed to them that every second the temperature was rising.

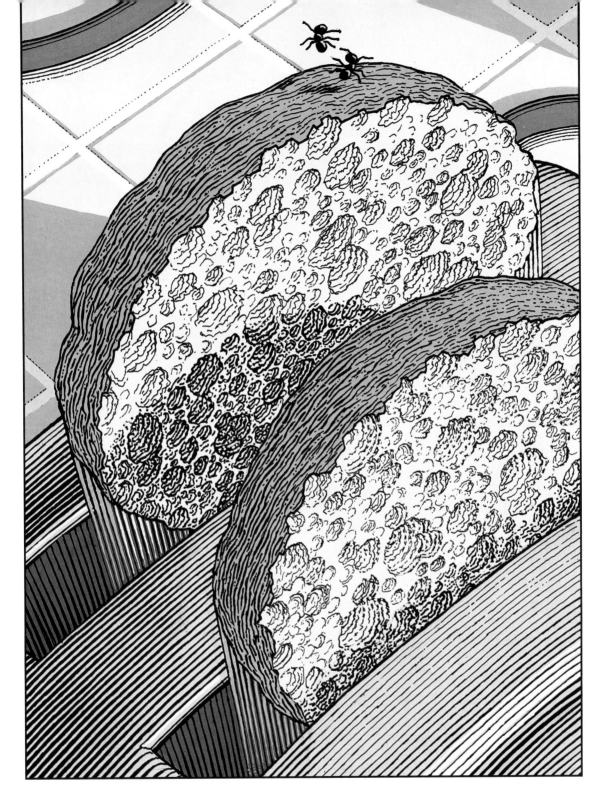

It soon became so unbearably hot that they thought they would soon be cooked. But suddenly the disk they were standing on rocketed upward and the two hot ants went flying through the air.

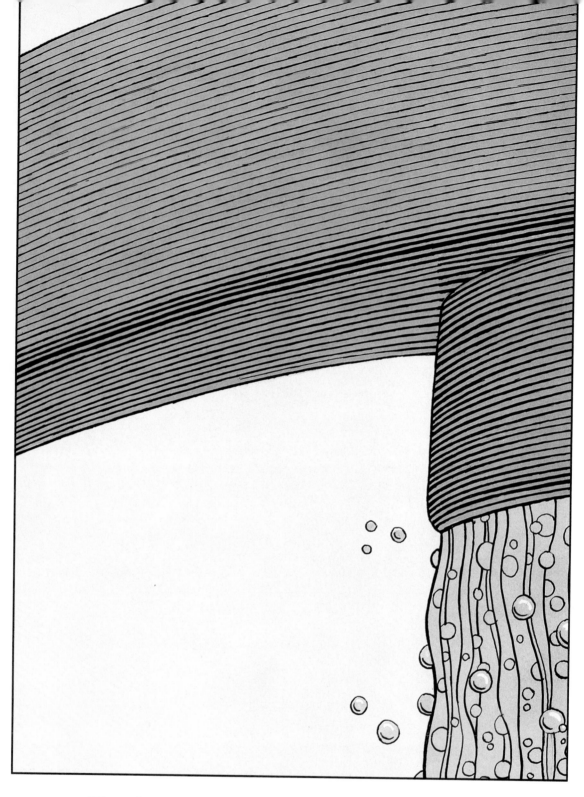

They landed near what seemed to be a
fountain—a waterfall pouring from a silver tube.
Both ants had a powerful thirst and longed to dip
their feverish heads into the refreshing water.
They quickly climbed along the tube.

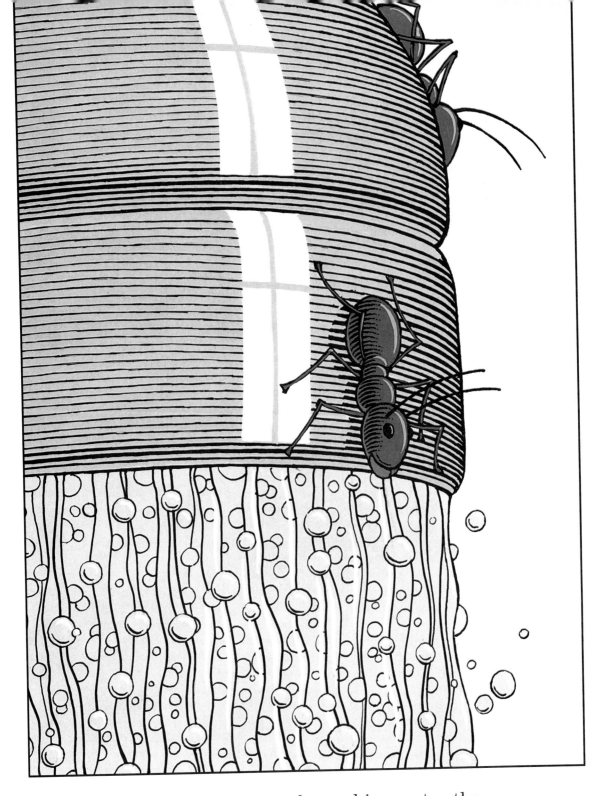

As they got closer to the rushing water the ants felt a cool spray. They tightly gripped the shiny surface of the fountain and slowly leaned their heads into the falling stream. But the force of the water was much too strong.

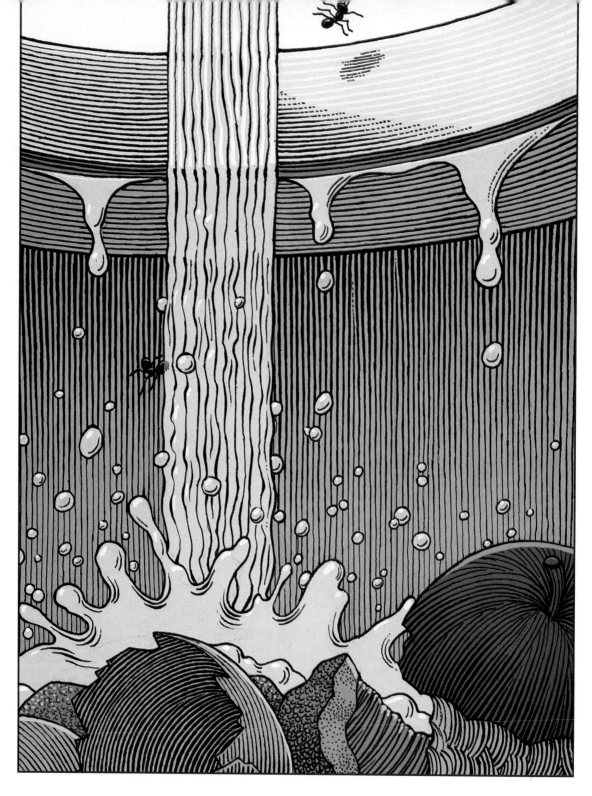

The tiny insects were pulled off the fountain
and plunged down into a wet, dark chamber. They
landed on half-eaten fruit and other soggy things.
Suddenly the air was filled with loud, frightening
sounds. The chamber began to spin.

The ants were caught in a whirling storm of shredded food and stinging rain. Then, just as quickly as it had started, the noise and spinning stopped. Bruised and dizzy, the ants climbed out of the chamber.

In daylight once again, they raced through
puddles and up a smooth metal wall. In the
distance they saw something comforting—two long,
narrow holes that reminded them of the warmth
and safety of their old underground home. They
climbed up into the dark openings.

But there was no safety inside these holes. A strange force passed through the wet ants. They were stunned senseless and blown out of the holes like bullets from a gun. When they landed the tiny insects were too exhausted to go on. They crawled into a dark corner and fell fast asleep.

Night had returned when the battered ants awoke to a familiar sound—the footsteps of their fellow insects returning for more crystals. The two ants slipped quietly to the end of the line. They climbed the glassy wall and once again stood amid the treasure. But this time they each chose a single crystal and followed their friends home.

Standing at the edge of their ant hole, the
two ants listened to the joyful sounds that came
from below. They knew how grateful their
mother queen would be when they gave her
their crystals. At that moment, the two ants felt
happier than they'd ever felt before. This was
their home, this was their family. This was
where they were meant to be.

An Ant

Watching an ant
I often feel
Like voicing an apology
Toward this little being.

Life is life to any creature
Big or small.
The difference is only
In the size of its container,
And mine happens to be so ridiculously,
Enormously big.

Michio Mado

Discovering Ants

by Christopher O'Toole

Illustrations by Wendy Meadway

The Life of a Worker

Worker ants do all the "household" duties. They keep the nest clean, repair any damage and build new sections to house the growing colony.

Another important job is the care of eggs and larvae. Workers on nursery duty lick the eggs and larvae frequently to keep them free from mold and tiny insects called mites. The larvae are fed on liquid food from the mouths of workers.

Workers have jobs to do outside the nest, too. They

An ant with nectar in its jaws.

visit flowers for nectar. They also gather honeydew from aphids. Some are scavengers and others kill for food. Some special kinds of ants, called harvester ants, collect and store seeds.

You will usually find a lot of ants at a source of food. This is because a worker can direct other workers from the nest to the food she has found. There are three ways of doing this. A large worker may simply carry a smaller one to the food.

Army ant soldiers and workers with their prey, a grasshopper.

Some species use tandem running; a returned worker tugs the antennae of another ant, which follows her, keeping in constant touch with her antennae, until they reach the food. Other kinds, like the red and black garden ants, lay a trail of scent from the food source to the nest. The workers quickly follow it and find the food.

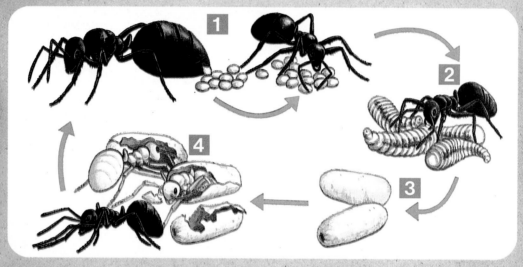

The life cycle of an ant

1 queen lays eggs
2 workers tend larvae
3 pupae

4 adults emerge from pupae and gradually harden and darken.

In the Ground

Many kinds of ants nest in the soil. Often, the nest is dug underneath a flat stone or a log. Under paving stones in gardens are favorite places, especially for the black garden ant. Workers of this ant often come indoors to find sugar and crumbs.

The nest of the black garden ant is 2 to 5 cm (1 to 2 in) deep and consists of lots of chambers or cells joined by interlocking tunnels. Sometimes there are so many tunnels that the nest looks like a sponge. The chambers are used to keep eggs and larvae in separate groups. The larvae themselves are kept in groups according to age.

Nursery workers also move the young around the nest so that they can enjoy the best temperatures for growth. You can test this yourself. Look under a flat stone covering an ant nest. If it is a warm day, but not too hot, you will see the eggs and larvae all in their separate groups just under the stone. Take a look later in the evening, when it is cooler. The nest will appear deserted,

An ant nest in the Sahara Desert.

because the workers will have taken the young into deeper and warmer chambers in the soil.

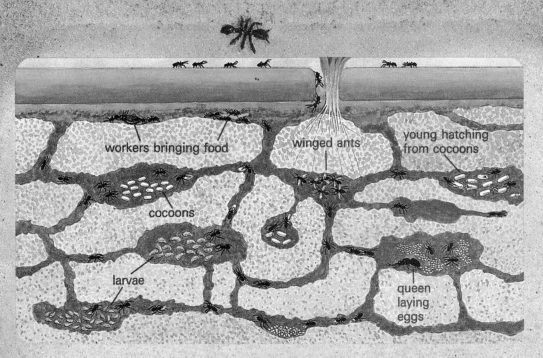

workers bringing food

winged ants

young hatching from cocoons

cocoons

larvae

queen laying eggs

If you could look into an ant nest under the ground this is what you might see.

MEET
ARLINE AND JOSEPH BAUM

Arline and Joseph Baum are a husband-and-wife team who are fascinated by the art of illusion. Arline Baum once worked as an assistant to a magician. Joseph Baum was an art director for an advertising agency. His ability to create illusions with art won him many awards.

In *Opt: An Illusionary Tale,* the Baums have created a land of optical illusions. The book begins like this: "Seeing is believing, but sometimes our eyes deceive us. When this happens, it is called an optical illusion. Opt is a land of optical illusions." This book won an award for being an outstanding science trade book.

OPT

AN ILLUSIONARY TALE

BY ARLINE AND JOSEPH BAUM

A Sunny Day in Opt, a day of banners, balloons, and surprises

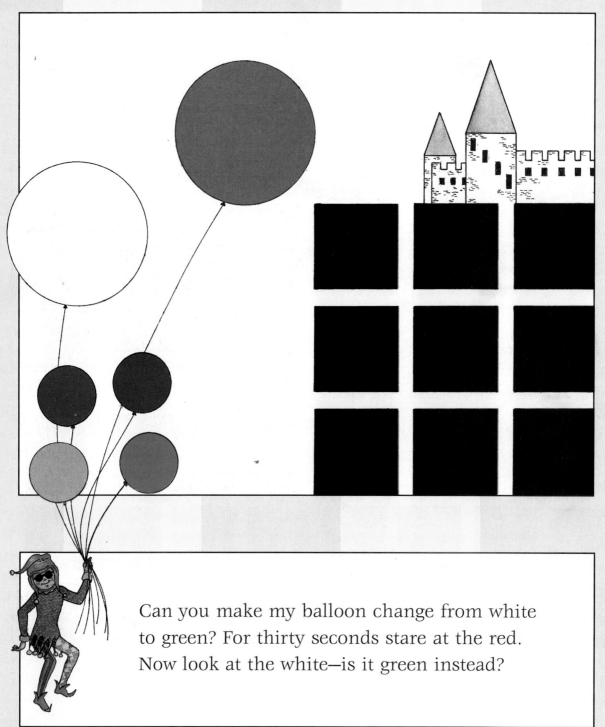

Can you make my balloon change from white to green? For thirty seconds stare at the red. Now look at the white—is it green instead?

The Wall surrounding the castle

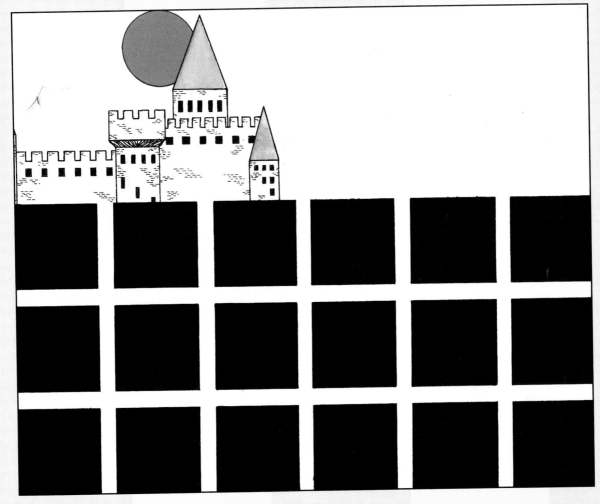

Where white lines cross, gray dots are seen.
One disappears where one has been.

The Castle Guard with his trident

How many prongs do you see?
I see two on the bottom—but on the top, three.

The Royal Messenger arriving with a letter for the King

The vertical lines of the messenger's cloak are crooked.
The red tape on the letter is longer than the blue.
But is this really true?
Remember, now you are in OPT!

The Trumpeters announcing the arrival of the messenger

Who is smaller?

The King and Queen waiting for the message

Who is taller?

The Message for the King to read

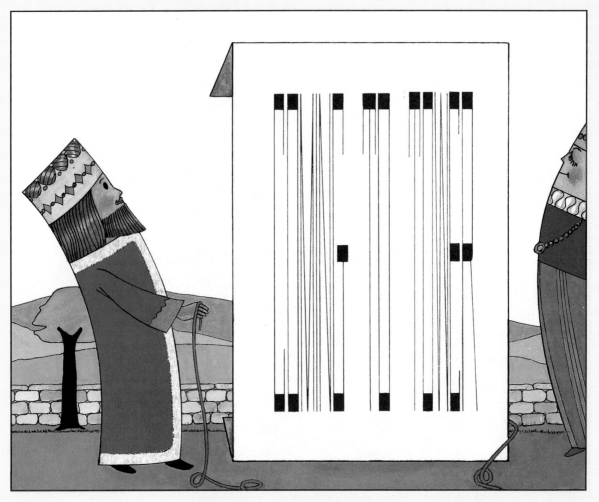

A clue to make the message clear.
First tilt the book, then take a look.
Who sent the message?

The Royal Art Gallery, dusted and tidied

Are the top of the lampshade and the top of the lamp base the same length?
Two ladies framed—or is it four?
Hidden elsewhere, you'll see two more.

The Prince goes fishing with his new rod

Which is the rod and which the branch of the tree?
Now look at the Prince's shirt.
What do you see?
Is the space between the shirt's black dots
larger than those same black spots?

The Princess picking a special bouquet

Flowers fair, flowers bright.
Which flower center is larger—
the black or the white?

The Great Hall, ready for the party

Should the Queen straighten the mirror on the wall?
There are eight more faces.
Can you find them all?

The Opt Sign pointing the way to the zoo

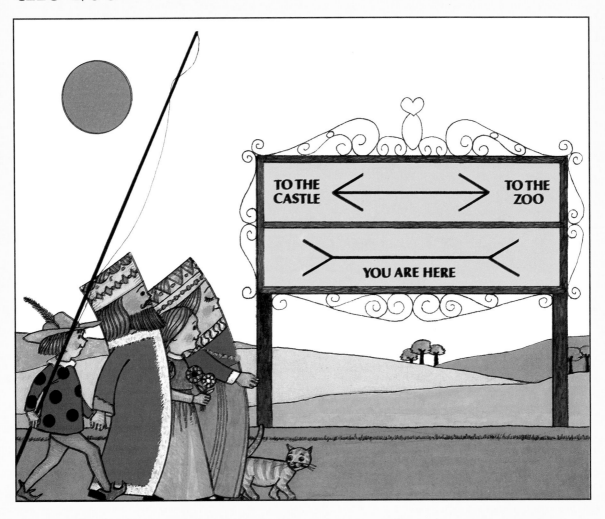

By the sign the royal family will stop.
Which line is longer, the bottom or top?
The King knows who the guest will be.
So do I—just follow me.

The Opt Zoo, home of amazing animals

Faces within faces can be found—
if you just turn the book around.
Is the body of the royal pet shorter than its neck?
Is the height of the zookeeper's hat the same as

The Zookeeper and the Royal Pet hearing the news

the width of its brim?
For thirty seconds stare at the star that is blue.
Now look at white paper—a colorful change,
just for you.

The Pavilion decorated with banners

Are the banners light green or dark green,
light pink or dark pink?
Some say they're the same shade.
But what do *you* think?

The Tower with guard spotting the guest

The guard marches up, stair by stair—
but is he getting anywhere?
He sees the guest.
Who can it be?
Turn the page and you will see!

The Guest is here!

The fire-snorting dragon now comes in.
Turn the book and his eyes will spin.
Arriving with presents—and none too late.
But did he tie the red ribbons on straight?

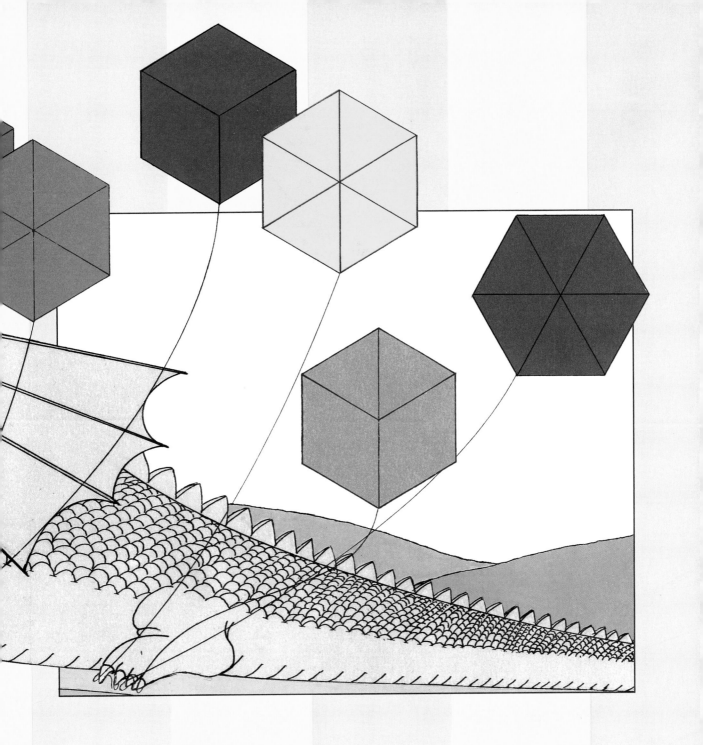

Look closely at the bright kites in the air.
Do flat kites or box kites float up there?

The Birthday Party for the Prince

This gift, unwrapped, tells the Prince's age.
This is what the dragon said,
"Six blocks become seven if you stand on your head.
HAPPY BIRTHDAY!"

The Dragon saying good-bye

The dragon was a perfect guest.
The party was a great success.
But *you* don't have to go away,
come join me in Opt any day.

HOUSES

Houses are faces
(haven't you found?)
with their hats in the air,
and their necks in the ground.

Windows are noses,
windows are eyes,
and doors are the mouths
of a suitable size.

And a porch—or the place
where porches begin—
is just like a mustache
shading the chin.

Aileen Fisher

PUZZLE

Map of a city with streets meeting at center?

Net to catch people jumping from a burning building?

Spider's web?

Burner on an electric stove?

Fingerprint?

No.

Frozen puddle after a hit by a rock.

A
SEEING
POEM

A SEEING POEM HAPPENS WHEN WORDS TAKE A SHAPE THAT HELPS THEM TO TURN ON A LIGHT IN SOMEONE'S MIND

Robert Froman

Meet
Alison Alexander and Susie Bower

▶ Can science be fun? To Alison
Alexander and Susie Bower, it's more
than fun–it's magic! A few years ago,
Alexander, a science teacher, and Bower, a
journalist, decided to help their own children
discover more about science. They put their
heads together and created some amazing science
experiments just for kids. The result was *Science
Magic*. Alexander and Bower believe that anyone
can become a science magician with the help
of a few simple materials.

SCIENCE MAGIC

by Alison Alexander and Susie Bower

Science helps us learn about nature. Magic tries to make us believe that things are not always what they seem to be. This next selection mixes both. The result? Some experiments that challenge what we see.

On a Sunny Day Make a Rainbow

You will need:
- ▶ mirror
- ▶ bright sunshine
- ▶ small mixing bowl (the size of the bowl will depend on the size of your mirror)

1 Fill the bowl half way with water and place it near a window in direct sun.

Hold the mirror in the water at an angle so that the sun shines directly onto it. You will have to move the mirror gently about until the colors of the rainbow begin to appear on the wall.

2 Lean the mirror against the side of the bowl without disturbing the water too much. When the water stops moving, you should be able to see the colors of the rainbow—red, orange, yellow, green, blue, indigo, violet. As the sun goes behind a cloud, the colors will fade.

You can make a rainbow in the garden. Wait until the sun begins to go down and then stand with your back to the sun and spray a shower of water through a hose pipe. As the sun shines on the water drops, the colors of the rainbow appear in the spray.

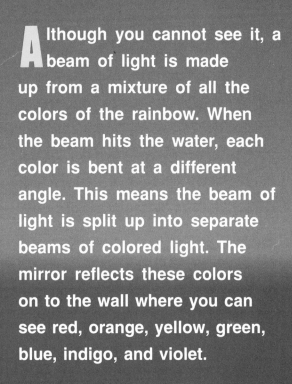

Although you cannot see it, a beam of light is made up from a mixture of all the colors of the rainbow. When the beam hits the water, each color is bent at a different angle. This means the beam of light is split up into separate beams of colored light. The mirror reflects these colors on to the wall where you can see red, orange, yellow, green, blue, indigo, and violet.

If you use a hose, the drops of water from the spray bend the beam of light and split it up into colors in the same way as the water in the bowl does. This forms a rainbow.

Watch the Colors Disappear

You will need:
- ► colored crayons or paints
- ► scissors
- ► cardboard
  (cereal packet is fine)
- ► ruler
- ► jam jar lid
- ► large-eyed needle
  (wool needle is ideal)
- ► length of wool about 3 feet
  (1 meter) long

1▶ Draw a circle on the cardboard using the jam jar lid and cut it out.

3▶ Mark the center of the cardboard circle. Divide the circle into six parts and color each section differently using the colors of the rainbow— red, orange, yellow, green, blue, violet. You can color the sections using just red, blue, green, red, blue, green.

2▶ Find the center by cutting a similar-sized circle in paper and folding it into quarters. Open it out and the point where the lines cross is the center.

4 With the needle or the point of the scissors, make two small holes either side of the center of the circle, one-half inch (1 cm) apart. Thread the wool through both holes and knot the ends together to make a loop.

5 Put one finger in each loop and twist up the wool by spinning your hands round. By moving your hands together and apart again you can make the disc spin. All the colors will disappear as the disc spins, and it will look as though it is white.

When the disc is spinning, all the colors go round very fast. You see them all at the same time and your eyes cannot see each different color separately. So you think the disc has no color at all and, to your eyes, it looks white.

Make a
Kaleidoscope

You will need:
- ► 2 handbag mirrors the same size (oblong are best)
- ► a piece of cardboard the same size as the mirrors
- ► greaseproof paper
- ► plastic wrap
- ► cellophane tape
- ► scissors
- ► small shapes of colored paper, beads, tin foil, or other tiny objects

1 ► Lay the cardboard on the table and place the mirrors face down on either side of it. Tape them all together.

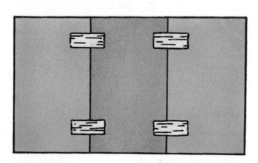

2 ► Turn over the mirrors and cardboard and bend the mirrors together to make a triangle, so that the mirrors are inside the triangle. Tape them together.

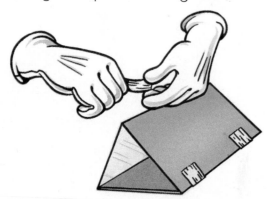

3 ► Tape the greaseproof paper tightly across one end of the kaleidoscope.

4 Put a few small pieces of colored paper into the kaleidoscope.

5 Stretch a piece of plastic wrap across the opening to stop the paper bits from falling out.

6 Look down into the kaleidoscope and watch the patterns change as you shake it.

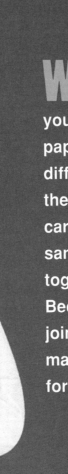

When you look down into the kaleidoscope, you can see the bits of paper you put in and six different reflections of them. The mirrors and the cardboard are all exactly the same size and, when fixed together, make a triangle. Because the mirrors are joined in this way, they can make many reflections which form a circle of pictures.

Peek Around the Corner with a Periscope

You will need:
- ► nail scissors
- ► 2 handbag mirrors (square ones are best)
- ► ruler
- ► oblong cracker box
- ► cellophane tape
- ► pencil

1▶ Near the top of the one side of the box, measure a 2-inch (5 cm) square window and cut it out. On the same side cut a slit 2 inches (5 cm) from the bottom of the box, as in the drawing.

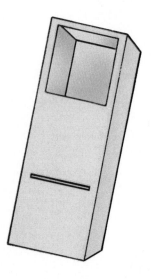

2▶ Turn the box around and on the opposite side cut another 2-inch (5 cm) square window near the bottom of the box. Cut a slit 2 inches (5 cm) from the top, as in the drawing. (It doesn't matter if your windows are not completely square.) Slide a mirror through each slit and place it diagonally between the slit and window. The top mirror must face downwards and the bottom mirror upwards.

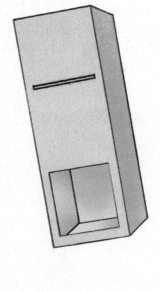

3▶ Tape the mirrors to the box. The edges may jut out of the slits.

4▶ Sit under the table and hold the periscope so that one window is above the table top. Look through the bottom mirror and you will be able to see what is on the table. You can also use the periscope to peek around a corner or over the heads of a crowd of people.

When the end of a periscope is pointed round a corner, the view will be reflected in the top mirror. The two mirrors in the periscope are fixed facing each other, and they slope at the same angle. This means that the bottom mirror will reflect the view from the top mirror. By looking in the bottom mirror, you can see the hidden view.

Acrobatic Pictures

You will need:
- ▶ a small notebook or some sheets of paper folded up to make a booklet
- ▶ pencils

1 ▶ In the top right-hand corner of each page, draw a ball, changing its position a little every time. Bend the corner of the book back and flick the pages. The ball will bounce up and down on the page.

2 ▶ You can turn the ball into a face with sad and happy expressions. You can also draw pin men jumping up and down. But you must remember to change the picture slightly each time.

The pictures flick past your eyes too quickly to see them separately. As the ball is in a slightly different position in each picture, it appears as if the ball is bouncing up and down.

193

SUNFLAKES

If sunlight fell like snowflakes,

gleaming yellow and so bright,

we could build a sunman,

we could have a sunball fight,

we could watch the sunflakes

drifting in the sky.

We could go sleighing

in the middle of July

through sundrifts and sunbanks,

we could ride a sunmobile,

and we could touch sunflakes—

I wonder how they'd feel.

Frank Asch

Unit 3

Family
Album

VALERIE FLOURNOY

Valerie Flournoy was thinking about the members of her own family when she wrote *The Patchwork Quilt*. She was especially remembering her Grandma Buchanan and how much fun they had had together when Valerie was growing up.

Flournoy hopes children who read her story will have respect "not only for their own parents and grandparents but for all of their 'family'—their ancestors—who have gone before them."

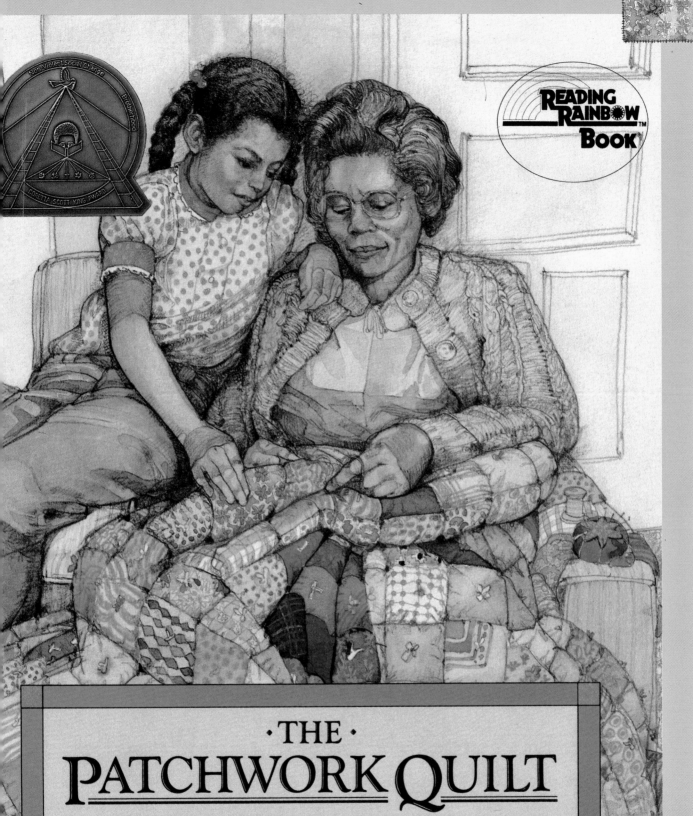

· THE ·
PATCHWORK QUILT

by VALERIE FLOURNOY

pictures by JERRY PINKNEY

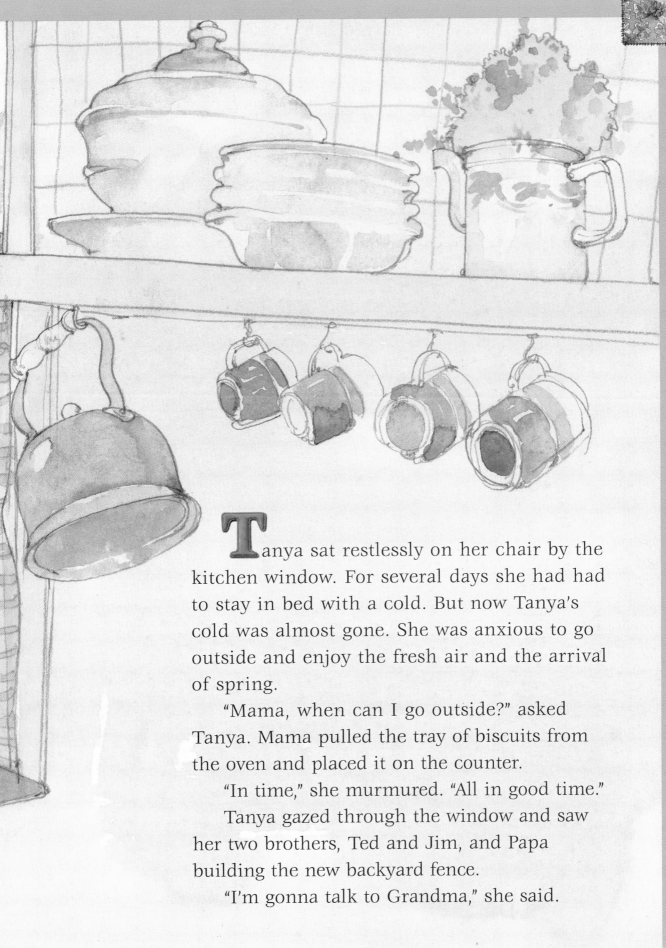

Tanya sat restlessly on her chair by the kitchen window. For several days she had had to stay in bed with a cold. But now Tanya's cold was almost gone. She was anxious to go outside and enjoy the fresh air and the arrival of spring.

"Mama, when can I go outside?" asked Tanya. Mama pulled the tray of biscuits from the oven and placed it on the counter.

"In time," she murmured. "All in good time."

Tanya gazed through the window and saw her two brothers, Ted and Jim, and Papa building the new backyard fence.

"I'm gonna talk to Grandma," she said.

Grandma was sitting in her favorite spot—the big soft chair in front of the picture window. In her lap were scraps of materials of all textures and colors. Tanya recognized some of them. The plaid was from Papa's old work shirt, and the red scraps were from the shirt Ted had torn that winter.

"Whatcha gonna do with all that stuff?" Tanya asked.

"Stuff? These ain't stuff. These little pieces gonna make me a quilt, a patchwork quilt."

Tanya tilted her head. "I know what a quilt is, Grandma. There's one on your bed, but it's old and dirty and Mama can never get it clean."

Grandma sighed. "It ain't dirty, honey. It's worn, the way it's supposed to be."

Grandma flexed her fingers to keep them from stiffening. She sucked in some air and said, "My mother made me a quilt when I wasn't any older than you. But sometimes the old ways are forgotten."

Tanya leaned against the chair and rested her head on her grandmother's shoulder.

Just then Mama walked in with two glasses of milk and some biscuits. Mama looked at the scraps of material that were scattered all over. "Grandma," she said, "I just cleaned this room, and now it's a mess."

"It's not a mess, Mama," Tanya said through a mouthful of biscuit. "It's a quilt."

"A quilt! You don't need these scraps. I can get you a quilt," Mama said.

Grandma looked at her daughter and then turned to her grandchild. "Yes, your mama can get you a quilt from any department store. But it won't be like my patchwork quilt, and it won't last as long either."

Mama looked at Grandma, then picked up Tanya's empty glass and went to make lunch.

Grandma's eyes grew dark and distant. She turned away from Tanya and gazed out the window, absent-mindedly rubbing the pieces of material through her fingers.

"Grandma, I'll help you make your quilt," Tanya said.

"Thank you, honey."

"Let's start right now. We'll be finished in no time."

Grandma held Tanya close and patted her head. "It's gonna take quite a while to make this quilt, not a couple of days or a week—not even a month. A good quilt, a masterpiece . . ." Grandma's eyes shone at the thought. "Why I need more material. More gold and blue, some red and green. And I'll need the time to do it right. It'll take me a year at least."

"A year," shouted Tanya. "That's too long. I can't wait that long, Grandma."

Grandma laughed. "A year ain't that long, honey. Makin' this quilt gonna be a joy. Now run along and let Grandma rest." Grandma turned her head toward the sunlight and closed her eyes.

"I'm gonna make a masterpiece," she murmured, clutching a scrap of cloth in her hand, just before she fell asleep.

"**W**e'll have to get you a new pair and use these old ones for rags," Mama said as she hung the last piece of wash on the clothesline one August afternoon.

Jim was miserable. His favorite blue corduroy pants had been held together with patches; now they were beyond repair.

"Bring them here," Grandma said.

Grandma took part of the pant leg and cut a few blue squares. Jim gave her a hug and watched her add his patches to the others.

"A quilt won't forget. It can tell your life story," she said.

The arrival of autumn meant school and Halloween. This year Tanya would be an African princess. She danced around in the long, flowing robes Mama had made from several yards of colorful material. The old bracelets and earrings Tanya had found in a trunk in the attic jingled noisily as she moved. Grandma cut some squares out of the leftover scraps and added Tanya to the quilt too!

The days grew colder but Tanya and her brothers didn't mind. They knew snow wasn't far away. Mama dreaded winter's coming. Every year she would plead with Grandma to move away from the drafty window, but Grandma wouldn't budge.

"Grandma, please," Mama scolded. "You can sit here by the heater."

"I'm not your grandmother, I'm your mother," Grandma said. "And I'm gonna sit here in the Lord's light and make my masterpiece."

It was the end of November when Ted, Jim, and Tanya got their wish. They awoke one morning to find everything in sight covered with snow. Tanya got dressed and flew down the stairs. Ted and Jim, and even Mama and Papa, were already outside.

"I don't like leaving Grandma in that house by herself," Mama said. "I know she's lonely."

Tanya pulled herself out of the snow being careful not to ruin her angel. "Grandma isn't lonely," Tanya said happily. "She and the quilt are telling each other stories."

Mama glanced questioningly at Tanya, "Telling each other stories?"

"Yes, Grandma says a quilt never forgets!"

The family spent the morning and most of the afternoon sledding down the hill. Finally, when they were all numb from the cold, they went inside for hot chocolate and sandwiches.

"I think I'll go sit and talk to Grandma," Mama said.

"Then she can explain to you about our quilt—our very own family quilt," Tanya said.

Mama saw the mischievous glint in her youngest child's eyes.

"Why, I may just have her do that, young lady," Mama said as she walked out of the kitchen.

Tanya leaned over the table to see into the living room. Grandma was hunched over, her eyes close to the fabric as she made tiny stitches. Mama sat at the old woman's feet. Tanya couldn't hear what was said but she knew Grandma was telling Mama all about quilts and how *this* quilt would be very special. Tanya sipped her chocolate slowly, then she saw Mama pick up a piece of fabric, rub it with her fingers, and smile.

From that moment on both women spent their winter evenings working on the quilt. Mama did the sewing while Grandma cut the fabrics and placed the scraps in a pattern of colors. Even while they were cooking and baking all their Christmas specialties during the day, at night they still worked on the quilt. Only once did Mama put it aside. She wanted to wear something special Christmas night, so she bought some gold material and made a beautiful dress. Tanya knew without asking that the gold scraps would be in the quilt too.

There was much singing and laughing that Christmas. All Grandma's sons and daughters and nieces and nephews came to pay their respects. The Christmas tree lights shone brightly, filling the room with sparkling colors. Later, when everyone had gone home, Papa said he had never felt so much happiness in the house. And Mama agreed.

When Tanya got downstairs the next morning, she found Papa fixing pancakes.

"Is today a special day too?" asked Jim.

"Where's Mama?" asked Tanya.

"Grandma doesn't feel well this morning," Papa said. "Your mother is with her now till the doctor gets here."

"Will Grandma be all right?" Ted asked.

Papa rubbed his son's head and smiled. "There's nothing for you to worry about. We'll take care of Grandma."

Tanya looked into the living room. There on the back of the big chair rested the patchwork quilt. It was folded neatly, just as Grandma had left it.

"Mother didn't want us to know she wasn't feeling well. She thought it would spoil our Christmas," Mama told them later, her face drawn and tired, her eyes a puffy red. "Now it's up to all of us to be quiet and make her as comfortable as possible." Papa put an arm around Mama's shoulder.

"Can we see Grandma?" Tanya asked.

"No, not tonight," Papa said. "Grandma needs plenty of rest."

It was nearly a week, the day before New Year's, before the children were permitted to see their grandmother. She looked tired and spoke in whispers.

"We miss you, Grandma," Ted said.

"And your muffins and hot chocolate," added Jim. Grandma smiled.

"Your quilt misses you too, Grandma," Tanya said. Grandma's smile faded from her lips. Her eyes grew cloudy.

"My masterpiece," Grandma sighed. "It would have been beautiful. Almost half finished." The old woman closed her eyes and turned away from her grandchildren. Papa whispered it was time to leave. Ted, Jim, and Tanya crept from the room.

Tanya walked slowly to where the quilt lay. She had seen Grandma and Mama work on it. Tanya thought real hard. She knew how to cut the scraps, but she wasn't certain of the rest. Just then Tanya felt a hand resting on her shoulder. She looked up and saw Mama.

"Tomorrow," Mama said.

New Year's Day was the beginning. After the dishes were washed and put away, Tanya and Mama examined the quilt.

"You cut more squares, Tanya, while I stitch some patches together," Mama said.

Tanya snipped and trimmed the scraps of material till her hands hurt from the scissors. Mama watched her carefully, making sure the squares were all the same size. The next day was the same as the last. More snipping and cutting. But Mama couldn't always be around to watch Tanya work. Grandma had to be looked after. So Tanya worked by herself. Then one night, as Papa read them stories, Jim walked over and looked at the quilt. In it he saw patches of blue. His blue. Without saying a word Jim picked up the scissors and some scraps and started to make squares. Ted helped Jim put the squares in piles while Mama showed Tanya how to join them.

Every day, as soon as she got home from school, Tanya worked on the quilt. Ted and Jim were too busy with sports, and Mama was looking after Grandma, so Tanya worked alone. But after a few weeks she stopped. Something was wrong—something was missing, Tanya thought. For days the quilt lay on the back of the chair. No one knew why Tanya had stopped working. Tanya would sit and look at the quilt. Finally she knew. Some*thing* wasn't missing. Some*one* was missing from the quilt.

That evening before she went to bed Tanya tiptoed into Grandma's room, a pair of scissors in her hand. She quietly lifted the end of Grandma's old quilt and carefully removed a few squares.

February and March came and went as Mama proudly watched her daughter work on the last few rows of patches. Tanya always found time for the quilt. Grandma had been watching too. The old woman had been getting stronger and stronger as the months passed. Once she was able, Papa would carry Grandma to her chair by the window. "I needs the Lord's light," Grandma said. Then she would sit and hum softly to herself and watch Tanya work.

"Yes, honey, this quilt is nothin' but a joy," Grandma said.

Summer vacation was almost here. One June day Tanya came home to find Grandma working on the quilt again! She had finished sewing the last few squares together; the stuffing was in place, and she was already pinning on the backing.

"Grandma!" Tanya shouted.

Grandma looked up. "Hush, child. It's almost time to do the quilting on these patches. But first I have some special finishing touches . . ."

The next night Grandma cut the final thread with her teeth. "There. It's done," she said. Mama helped Grandma spread the quilt full length.

Nobody had realized how big it had gotten or how beautiful. Reds, greens, blues, and golds, light shades and dark, blended in and out throughout the quilt.

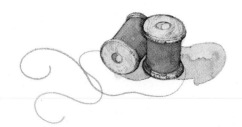

"It's beautiful," Papa said. He touched the gold patch, looked at Mama, and remembered. Jim remembered too. There was his blue and the red from Ted's shirt. There was Tanya's Halloween costume. And there was Grandma. Even though her patch was old, it fit right in.

They all remembered the past year. They especially remembered Tanya and all her work. So it had been decided. In the right hand corner of the last row of patches was delicately stitched, "For Tanya from your Mama and Grandma."

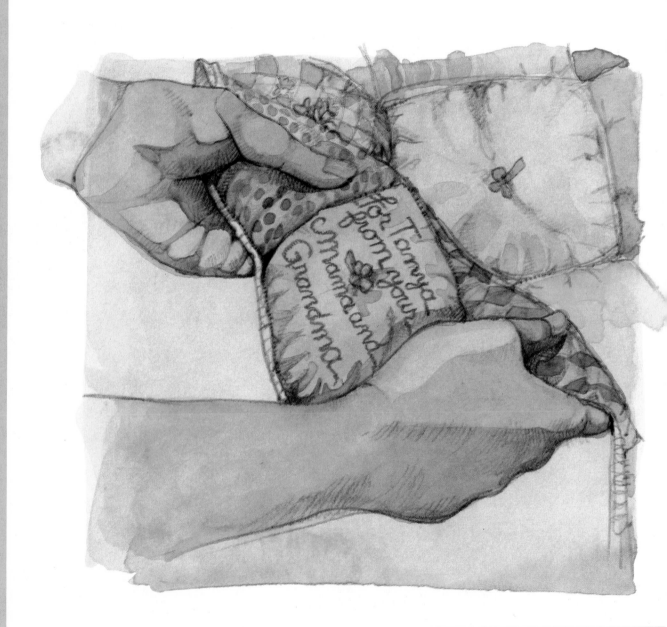

JERRY PINKNEY

Jerry Pinkney's elementary school teachers often asked him to draw on the chalkboard for class projects. The artist says that this made him feel special, because he has loved to draw for as long as he can remember.

Today Jerry Pinkney spends much of his time in libraries. He looks for information to add just the right details to his illustrations. You can see some of these details in *The Patchwork Quilt,* which won the Coretta Scott King Award for Illustration. Among the many other books the artist has illustrated are *Rabbit Makes a Monkey of Lion* and *Turtle in July.*

"WOOD" YOU

Crowing rooster
by the Blas family

María Jiménez Ojeda
putting finishing
touches on a carving

BELIEVE IT?

Dancing chickens! Purple lions! Kings and cactus! Where do they come from? How are they made?

Entire families in Mexico's Oaxaca Valley work together to produce these imaginative woodcarvings. With machetes and kitchen knives, some of the adults and teenagers carve the figures from copal wood. Younger children sand the figures smooth. At painting time, other members of the family take over. Even the family's farm animals help with the finishing touches. Trimmings from their hair are used to make tails, manes, and whiskers for the carvings.

Carving is not new to the Oaxacan people. For more than five hundred years, they have carved masks and miniature toys. What is new is that now people from other parts of the world are getting a chance to see and buy their woodcarvings.

*Patterned cat
by Margarito Melchor*

*Two dancing chickens
by Ventura Fabian*

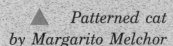

*Margarito Melchor
Fuentes and his wife
Maria Teresa Santiago
working on two carvings*

225

We laugh and cry,
We work and play,
We help each other
Every day.
The world's a lovely
Place to be
Because we are
A family.

Mary Ann Hoberman

En un barrio de
LOS ANGELES
(IN A NEIGHBORHOOD IN LOS ANGELES)

el español	I learned
lo aprendí	Spanish
de mi abuela	from my grandma
mijito	*mijito*
no llores	don't cry
me decía	she'd tell me
en las mañanas	on the mornings
cuando salían	my parents
mis padres	would leave
a trabajar	to work
en las canerías	at the fish
de pescado	canneries
mi abuela	my grandma
platicaba	would chat
con las sillas	with chairs
les cantaba	sing them
canciones	old
antiguas	songs
les bailaba	dance
valses en	waltzes with them
la cocina	in the kitchen
cuando decía	when she'd say
niño barrigón	*niño barrigón*
se reía	she'd laugh

con mi abuela	with my grandma
aprendí	I learned
a contar nubes	to count clouds
a reconocer	to point out
en las macetas	in flowerpots
la yerbabuena	mint leaves
mi abuela	my grandma
llevaba lunas	wore moons
en el vestido	on her dress
la montaña	Mexico's mountains
el desierto	deserts
el mar de México	ocean
en sus ojos	in her eyes
yo los veía	I'd see them
en sus trenzas	in her braids
yo los tocaba	I'd touch them
con su voz	in her voice
yo los olía	smell them
un día	one day
me dijeron:	I was told:
se fue muy lejos	she went far away
pero yo aún	but still
la siento	I feel her
conmigo	with me
diciéndome	whispering
quedito al oído	in my ear
mijito	*mijito*

Francisco X. Alarcón (translated by Francisco Aragon)

すきやき

Ina R. Friedman

How My Parents
Learned to Eat

Illustrated by Allen Say

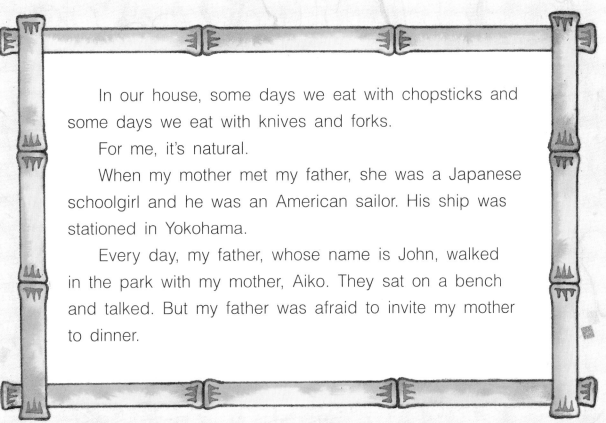

In our house, some days we eat with chopsticks and some days we eat with knives and forks.

For me, it's natural.

When my mother met my father, she was a Japanese schoolgirl and he was an American sailor. His ship was stationed in Yokohama.

Every day, my father, whose name is John, walked in the park with my mother, Aiko. They sat on a bench and talked. But my father was afraid to invite my mother to dinner.

If we go to a restaurant, he thought, I'll go hungry because I don't know how to eat with chopsticks. And if I go hungry, I'll act like a bear. Then Aiko won't like me. I'd better not ask her to dinner.

My mother wondered why my father never invited her to dinner. Perhaps John is afraid I don't know how to eat with a knife and fork and I'll look silly, she thought. Maybe it is best if he doesn't invite me to dinner.

So they walked and talked and never ate a bowl of rice or a piece of bread together.

One day, the captain of my father's ship said, "John, in three weeks the ship is leaving Japan."

My father was sad. He wanted to marry my mother. How can I ask her to marry me? he thought. I don't even know if we like the same food. And if we don't, we'll go hungry. It's hard to be happy if you're hungry. I'll have to find out what food she likes. And I'll have to learn to eat with chopsticks.

So he went to a Japanese restaurant.

Everyone sat on cushions around low tables. My father bowed to the waiter. "Please, teach me to eat with chopsticks."

"Of course," said the waiter, bowing.

The waiter brought a bowl of rice and a plate of sukiyaki. Sukiyaki is made of small pieces of meat, vegetables, and tofu. It smelled good. My father wanted to gobble it up.

The waiter placed two chopsticks between my father's fingers. "Hold the bottom chopstick still. Move the top one to pick up the food," the waiter said.

My father tried, but the meat slipped off his chopstick and fell on his lap.

The waiter came back with a bowl of soup. How can I eat soup with chopsticks? my father thought.

"Drink," said the waiter. "Drink from the bowl."

"Thank goodness," my father said. After the soup my father felt better. He picked up the chopsticks. Finally, my father put one piece of meat in his mouth. Delicious!

"More soup, please," he said.

After three bowls of soup my father felt much better. Then he practiced some more with his chopsticks. Soon, there was more sukiyaki in his belly than on the floor. But it was too late to call my mother. He had to run back to his ship.

That night, my mother was sad. Every other day my father had come to see her. That day he did not come. He did not call on the telephone. Perhaps he was tired of walking and talking. Perhaps he was ashamed of her because she did not know how to eat with a knife and fork. Perhaps his ship had sailed away. All night she could not sleep.

And all night my father sat on his bunk, pretending to pick up sukiyaki.

The next morning my father called my mother. "Please, will you eat dinner with me tonight?"

"Yes!" my mother shouted into the phone. First she was happy. Then she was afraid. She took her schoolbooks and ran to the house of Great Uncle.

Great Uncle had visited England. He had seen the British Museum. He had eaten dinners with Englishmen.

My mother knocked at the door. Great Uncle opened it.

"Why are you so sad, child?" he asked.

"Because I must learn to eat with a knife and fork by seven o'clock tonight."

Great Uncle nodded. "Foreign ways are quite strange. Why do you want to eat with a knife and fork?"

My mother blushed.

"Is it the American sailor?" Great Uncle asked. "I see. . . . Here, take this note to your teacher. At lunchtime I will come and take you to a foreign restaurant. By seven o'clock tonight you will eat with a knife and fork."

My mother picked up her school bag and bowed.

"No," Great Uncle stuck out his hand. "In the West you shake hands."

The restaurant had red carpets and many lights. Great Uncle pulled out a chair for my mother. "In the West, men help ladies into chairs," he told her.

My mother looked at the small fork and the large fork on the left. She looked at the knife, little spoon, and big spoon on the right. Her head grew dizzy.

"Different utensils for different foods," Great Uncle said.

"How strange to dirty so many things," said my mother. "A chopstick is a chopstick. I can eat everything with two chopsticks."

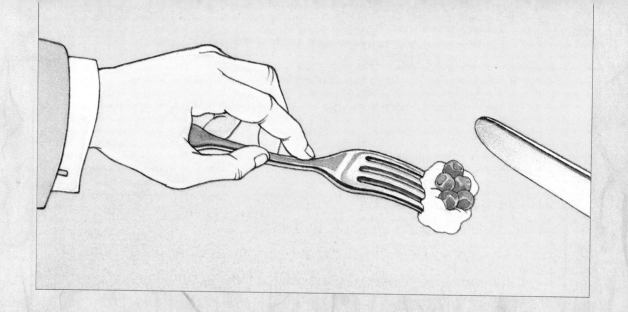

When the waiter brought the soup, Great Uncle pointed at the large spoon. "Dip it slowly, bring it to your mouth. Sip quietly."

My mother's hand trembled. The soup spilled onto the white cloth.

"You'll learn," Great Uncle encouraged her.

When my mother was finished with the soup, the waiter brought her a plate of mashed potatoes, roast beef, and peas.

"This is the way Westerners eat," Great Uncle said. "With the knife and fork they cut the meat. Then they hold the fork upside down in their left hand. Like birds, they build a nest of mashed potatoes. They put the peas in the nest with the knife. Then they slip the nest into their mouth. Try it."

The mashed potatoes were not difficult. But the peas rolled all over the plate. "Impossible," said my mother. "I'll never learn by seven o'clock tonight."

"You can learn anything," Great Uncle said. "Try again. More mashed potatoes and peas, please," he said to the waiter.

At seven o'clock my father came to see my mother.

"Why didn't you wear your kimono?" he asked. "We are going to a Japanese restaurant."

"A Japanese restaurant? Don't you think I know how to eat Western food?" my mother asked.

"Of course. Don't you think I know how to eat Japanese food?"

"Of course."

"Then, tonight we'll eat meat and potatoes. Tomorrow night we'll eat sukiyaki."

"Tomorrow night I will wear my kimono," my mother said. She started to bow. Then she stopped and put out her hand. My father shook it.

My father ordered two plates of mashed potatoes, roast beef, and peas. He watched my mother cut the meat into pieces. He stared when she turned over her fork and made a bird's nest. He was amazed.

"You are very clever with a knife and fork," he said.

"Thank you," said my mother.

"You must teach me," my father said. "That's a new way of eating peas."

"Teach you?"

"Yes, Americans don't eat that way." He slid his fork under some peas and put them in his mouth.

My mother stared at him. "But Great Uncle taught me. He lived in England. He knows the ways of the West."

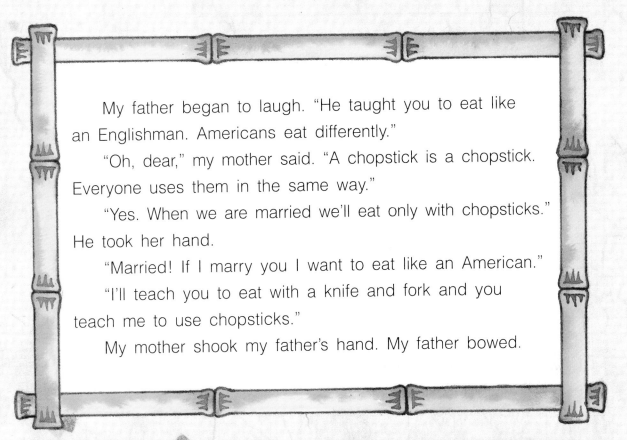

My father began to laugh. "He taught you to eat like an Englishman. Americans eat differently."

"Oh, dear," my mother said. "A chopstick is a chopstick. Everyone uses them in the same way."

"Yes. When we are married we'll eat only with chopsticks." He took her hand.

"Married! If I marry you I want to eat like an American."

"I'll teach you to eat with a knife and fork and you teach me to use chopsticks."

My mother shook my father's hand. My father bowed.

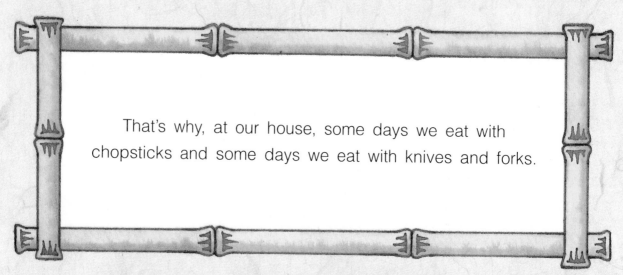

That's why, at our house, some days we eat with chopsticks and some days we eat with knives and forks.

MEET
INA R. FRIEDMAN

Sometimes a good friend can inspire a good book. Ina R. Friedman says, *"How My Parents Learned to Eat* grew out of my friendship with a Japanese woman who married an American. I thought how fortunate their children were to be brought up with two cultures."* Her story about how cultural understanding can start with everyday things won a Christopher Award.

MEET
ALLEN SAY

When Allen Say was twelve, a Japanese cartoonist taught him how to draw. Years later, Say drew pictures for many children's books. *How My Parents Learned to Eat* shows details that he remembered from growing up in Japan. *The Boy of the Three-Year Nap,* a Caldecott Honor Book, retells a Japanese folk tale. Say has said, "I look at my work as a personal tree-ring, a growth record."

Contact

Kids Dish Out Lunch Around the World

Hot Plates

by
Samantha
Bonar

Oh no!

Not another soggy tuna fish sandwich! Want to trade it for a vegemite sandwich? How about swapping it for some yucca? These are just a few of the tasty treats that kids in other countries munch at lunch. Check out some chow from around the world...

Dining Down Under

If you looked in a typical lunch box in Australia, you'd probably find a "vegemite" sandwich, "saltanas," "crisps" and a "popper."

Vegemite is a black, salty spread that looks like tar. It's made from yeast extract and tastes like beef stock.

"Anyone who hasn't grown up with it doesn't like it. It's kind of weird," admits Tessa Virtue, 12, who lives in Canberra, Australia. Saltanas are dried yellow grapes. And crisps are potato chips.

Ex-couscous Me!

In the North African country of Morocco, kids get a lunch break from noon to 2 p.m. Most head home, where they often eat tagine (a beef, lamb or vegetable stew).

Moroccans put a steamer full of couscous (say: *Koos-Koos*) over the tagine while it's cooking. Couscous is a pasta made of tiny granules of wheat. The spicy steam from the tagine flavors the

Australian kids eat up meat pies—beef and sauce baked in a pastry crust.

Gulp! He's popped a popper in his mouth!

Chips ahoy! Some kids like salt and vinegar crisps best.

This chiko roll is like an egg roll.

So what's a popper? The answer: a boxed fruit drink.

Australian kids usually bring their lunches to school. But they can also order food like meat pies from the school's tuck shop.

Kids stick the ketchup bottle right in the top of the meat pie and squirt. Then they eat the pie with their hands. Look Ma! No forks!

couscous. After it's cooked, you dump the couscous on a plate, make a little hollow, pour in the tagine—and eat it all with your hands!

Rachid Bouhamidi, 13, lives in California, but his dad is from

Morocco. Rachid likes couscous ("except when they put raisins in it. Yuck!"). But he likes b'stilla even better. "It's this pastry with eggs, chicken, and walnuts inside and cinnamon and sugar on top." Yum!

These Moroccan kids don't need an excuse to eat couscous!

B'stilla my heart! It's a pastry full of chicken and nuts with sugar on top.

247

Yummy Yucca?

Lunch is the biggest meal of the day in Brazil. First, soup might be served, then the main course of meat or fish with rice, beans and vegetables. Yucca, a desert plant, is a common side dish.

A favorite dish is feijoada (say: *fay-ZWAH-duh*). It's a stew of black beans and pork, served with veggies and rice.

"I like plain black beans and rice," said 11-year-old Joanna Comfort. Her mom is from Brazil. "I hate it when my mom makes bacalhau (dried codfish), because it smells funny!"

Brazilian kids eat a lot of fruit, such as bananas and mangoes. Their favorite drink is guarana soda. (Guarana is a nut harvested from the Amazon rain forest.) Or they might drink a shake made from avocados, milk and sugar cane. For dessert, the kids gobble up coconut pudim—a custard made with coconut milk. But they also love <u>ice cream</u>!

Watch Out for Kites!

Some moms in India get up as early as 5:30 a.m. to make lunch for their kids! That's because every morning they make chapatis and curries from scratch. Chapati is thin, crisp bread used to scoop up vegetables and curries. Curry is a spicy sauce. It might be made with chicken, pork, lamb, goat or vegetables. But most people in India never eat beef.

Loni Mahanta, 13, loves chicken curry. "I use this fried, puffy pastry to soak up the curry. Then I eat the chicken."

Loni's friend, Maya Sudhakar, 13, can't stand kerola. "It's this bumpy vegetable that's really bitter," she shudders.

Indian moms pack the fresh chapatis and curries in lunch boxes. Indian kids decorate their lunch boxes in bright colors.

They eat lunch while walking around or sitting on benches under trees. But Indian kids in the country have to keep an eye out for kites—big birds similar to eagles. They swoop down and snatch the food!

Open the hatch, through the gums, look out stomach, here the beans come!

Sukhi Bhaji (dry vegetables) with poori (bread) and hot mango pickle.

Kids in India eat with their right hands only. The rims of steel plates help scoop up food.

In Bombay, the *dubbawallas*, or "delivery people," drop off lunches by cart.

Lunch for Japanese kids isn't in the bag—it's in the obento!

What's for lunch? Cold rice with sesame seeds, fried goodies, vegetable salad and fresh fruit.

Girls at a high school in Japan meet 'n eat!

Is Today a Rice Day or a Bread Day?

Younger kids in Japan eat from trays at their classroom desks. Lunch is prepared in the school kitchen. Three days a week are "rice days," the other two are "bread days."

On rice days, kids use chopsticks and eat traditional Japanese foods, such as miso soup (made from soybean paste), fish and rice. On bread days, they use a knife and fork and eat Western foods like chicken, pork and loaves of bread. Japanese kids drink milk—no matter what day it is!

Ko Sugiyama, 10, from Saitama, Japan, loves fried potato balls. "First you scoop the potato out of the skin, then you mash it, roll it back up in the skin and deep-fry it 'til it's crisp," he explains. "I like mine with spicy black sauce."

High school kids almost always bring their own lunch. The lunch is packed in a lunch box called an obento. An obento has separate compartments for chopsticks and each dish. Older kids might pack cold rice, vegetable salad and sushi. What's sushi? Raw fish!

Want a bite of sushi? This roll has avocado, rice and fish eggs!

Invitation

Listen! I've a big surprise!

My new mom has light-green eyes

and my new brother, almost ten,

is really smart. He helped me when

we did our homework. They moved in

a week ago. When we begin

to settle down, she said that you

could come for dinner. When you do

you'll like them, just like Dad and me,

so come and meet my family!

Myra Cohn Livingston

RAMONA

FOREVER

by Beverly Cleary

It has been a year of many changes for Ramona Quimby and her family. Aunt Bea and Uncle Hobart are newly married, and they are headed north on their honeymoon. Ramona and her sister, Beezus, have tied their white shoes to the truck's bumper for good luck.

The family cat, Picky-picky, has died suddenly, but there is good news, too. Mr. Quimby has started a new job as the manager of a large food store, and Mrs. Quimby is going to have a baby. The Quimbys have even given the baby a name—baby Algie.

Ramona has mixed feelings about all the changes, especially baby Algie. How will it feel not to be the youngest anymore?

After the wedding, everyone felt let down, the way they always felt the day after Christmas, only worse. Nothing seemed interesting after so much excitement. Grandpa Day had flown back to his sunshine and shuffleboard. Mr. Quimby was at work all day. Friends had gone off to camp, to the mountains, or the beach. Howie and Willa Jean had gone to visit their other grandmother.

"Girls, please stop moping around," said Mrs. Quimby.

"We can't find anything to do," said Beezus.

Ramona was silent. If she complained, her mother would tell her to clean out her closet.

"Read a book," said Mrs. Quimby. "Both of you, read a book."

"I've read all my books a million times," said Ramona, who usually enjoyed rereading her favorites.

"Then go to the library." Mrs. Quimby was beginning to sound irritable.

"It's too hot," complained Ramona. Mrs. Quimby glanced at her watch.

"Mother, are you expecting someone?" asked Ramona. "You keep looking at your watch."

"I certainly am," said her mother. "A stranger." With a big sigh, Mrs. Quimby sank heavily to the couch, glanced at her watch again, and closed her eyes. The girls exchanged guilty looks. Their poor mother, worn out by Algie kicking her when there was so much of her to feel hot.

"Mother, are you all right?" Beezus sounded worried.

"I'm fine," snapped Mrs. Quimby, which surprised the girls into behaving.

That evening, the sisters helped their mother put together a cold supper of tuna fish salad and sliced tomatoes. While the family was eating, Mr. Quimby told them that now that the "Hawaiian Holidays" sale with bargains in fresh pineapple and papaya had come to an end, all the Shop-rite markets were preparing for "Western Bar-b-q Week" with specials on steak, baked beans, tomato sauce, and chili. He planned to paint bucking broncos on the front windows.

Mrs. Quimby nibbled at her salad and glanced at her watch.

"And everybody will see your paintings," said Ramona, happy that her father was now an artist as well as a market manager.

"Not quite the same as an exhibit in a museum," said Mr. Quimby, who did not sound as happy as Ramona expected.

Mrs. Quimby pushed her chair farther from the table and glanced at her watch. All eyes were on her.

"Shall I call the doctor?" asked Mr. Quimby.

"Please," said Mrs. Quimby as she rose from the table, hugged Algie, and breathed, "Oo-oo."

Ramona and Beezus, excited and frightened, looked at one another. At last! The fifth Quimby would soon be here. Nothing would be the same again, ever. Mr. Quimby reported that the doctor would meet them at the hospital. Without being asked, Beezus ran for the bag her mother had packed several weeks ago.

Mrs. Quimby kissed her daughters. "Don't look so frightened," she said. "Everything is going to be all right. Be good girls, and Daddy will be home as soon as he can." She bent forward and hugged Algie again.

The house suddenly seemed empty. The girls listened to the car back out of the driveway. The sound of the motor became lost in traffic.

"Well," said Beezus, "I suppose we might as well do the dishes."

"I suppose so." Ramona tested all the doors, including the door to the basement, to make sure they were locked.

"Too bad Picky-picky isn't here to eat all this tuna salad no one felt like eating." Beezus scraped the plates into the garbage.

To her own surprise, Ramona burst into tears and buried her face in a dish towel. "I just want Mother to come home," she wept.

Beezus wiped her soapy hands on the seat of her cutoff jeans. Then she put her arms around Ramona, something she had never done before. "Don't worry, Ramona. Everything will be all right. Mother said so, and I remember when you came."

Ramona felt better. A big sister could be a comfort if she wanted to.

"You got born and Mother was fine." Beezus handed Ramona a clean dish towel.

Minutes crawled by. The long Oregon dusk turned into night. The girls turned on the television set to a program about people in a hospital, running, shouting, giving orders. Quickly they turned it off. "I hope Aunt Bea and Uncle Hobart are all right," said Ramona. The girls longed for their loving aunt, who was cheerful in times of trouble and who was always there when the family needed her. Now she was in a truck, riding along the Canadian Highway to Alaska. Ramona thought about bears, mean bears. She wondered if two pairs of white shoes still danced from the bumper of the truck.

The ring of the telephone made Ramona feel as if arrows of electricity had shot through her stomach as Beezus ran to answer.

"Oh." There was disappointment in Beezus's voice. "All right, Daddy. No. No, we don't mind." When the conversation ended, she turned to Ramona, who was wild for news, and said, "Algie is taking his time. Daddy wants to stay with Mom and wanted to be sure we didn't mind staying alone. I said we didn't, and he said we were brave girls."

"Oh," said Ramona, who longed for her father's return. "Well, I'm brave, I guess." Even though the evening was unusually warm, she closed all the windows.

"I suppose we should go to bed," said Beezus. "If you want, you can get in bed with me.

"We better leave lights on for Daddy." Ramona turned on the porch light, as well as all the lights in the living room and hall, before she climbed into her sister's bed. "So Daddy won't fall over anything," she explained.

"Good idea," agreed Beezus. Each sister knew the other felt safer with the lights on.

"I hope Algie will hurry," said Ramona.

"So do I," agreed Beezus.

The girls slept lightly until the sound of a key in the door awoke them. "Daddy?" Beezus called out.

"Yes." Mr. Quimby came down the hall to the door of Beezus's room. "Great news.

Roberta Day Quimby,
six pounds, four ounces,
arrived safe and sound.
Your mother is fine."

Barely awake, Ramona asked,
"Who's Roberta?"

"Your new sister," answered her father,
"and my namesake."

"*Sister.*" Now Ramona was wide-awake. The
family had referred to the baby as Algie so long she
had assumed that of course she would have a brother.

"Yes, a beautiful little sister," said her father. "Now,
go back to sleep. It's four o'clock in the morning, and
I've got to get up at seven-thirty."

The next morning, Mr. Quimby overslept and ate
his breakfast standing up. He was halfway out the door
when he called back, "When I get off work, we'll have
dinner at the Whopperburger, and then we'll all go see
Roberta and your mother."

The day was long and lonely. Even a swimming
lesson at the park and a trip to the library did little to
make time pass. "I wonder what Roberta looks like?"
said Beezus.

"And whose room she will share when she outgrows
the bassinette?" worried Ramona.

The one happy moment in the day for the girls
was a telephone call from their mother, who reported
that Roberta was a beautiful, healthy little sister. She
couldn't wait to bring her home, and she was proud of

her daughters for being so good about staying alone. This pleased Beezus and Ramona so much they ran the vacuum cleaner and dusted, which made time pass faster until their father, looking exhausted, came home to take them out for hamburgers and a visit to the fifth Quimby.

Ramona could feel her heart pounding as she finally climbed the steps to the hospital. Visitors, some carrying flowers and others looking careworn, walked toward the elevators. Nurses hurried, a doctor was paged over the loudspeaker. Ramona could scarcely bear her own excitement. The rising of the elevator made her stomach feel as if it had stayed behind on the first floor. When the elevator stopped, Mr. Quimby led the way down the hall.

"Excuse me," called a nurse.

Surprised, the family stopped and turned.

"Children under twelve are not allowed to visit the maternity ward," said the nurse. "Little girl, you will have to go down and wait in the lobby."

"Why is that?" asked Mr. Quimby.

"Children under twelve might have contagious diseases," explained the nurse. "We have to protect the babies."

"I'm sorry, Ramona," said Mr. Quimby. "I didn't know. I am afraid you will have to do as the nurse says."

"Does she mean I'm *germy?*" Ramona was humiliated. "I took a shower this morning and washed my hands at the Whopperburger so I would be extra clean."

"Sometimes children are coming down with something and don't know it," explained Mr. Quimby. "Now, be a big girl and go downstairs and wait for us."

Ramona's eyes filled with tears of disappointment, but she found some pleasure in riding in the elevator alone. By the time she reached the lobby, she felt worse. The nurse called her a little girl. Her father called her a big girl. What was she? A germy girl.

Ramona sat gingerly on the edge of a Naugahyde couch. If she leaned back, she might get germs on it, or it might get germs on her. She swallowed hard. Was her throat a little bit sore? She thought maybe it was, way down in back. She put her hand to her forehead the way her mother did when she thought Ramona might have a fever. Her forehead was warm, maybe too warm.

As Ramona waited, she began to itch the way she itched when she had chickenpox. Her head itched, her back itched, her legs itched. Ramona scratched. A woman sat down on the couch, looked at Ramona, got up, and moved to another couch.

Ramona felt worse. She itched more and scratched harder. She swallowed often to see how her sore throat was coming along. She peeked down the neck of her blouse to see if she might have a rash and was surprised that she did not. She sniffed from time to time to see if she had a runny nose.

Now Ramona was angry. It would serve everybody right if she came down with some horrible disease, right there in their old hospital. That would show everybody how germfree the place was. Ramona squirmed and gave that hard-to-reach place between her shoulder blades a good hard scratch. Then she scratched her head with both hands. People stopped to stare.

A man in a white coat, with a stethoscope hanging out of his pocket, came hurrying through the lobby, glanced at Ramona, stopped, and took a good look at her. "How do you feel?" he asked.

"Awful," she admitted. "A nurse said I was too germy to go see my mother and new sister, but I think I caught some disease right here."

"I see," said the doctor. "Open your mouth and say 'ah.'"

Ramona *ahhed* until she gagged.

"Mh-hm," murmured the doctor. He looked so serious Ramona was alarmed. Then he pulled out his stethoscope and listened to her front and back, thumping as he did so. What was he hearing? Was there something wrong with her insides? Why didn't her father come?

The doctor nodded as if his worst suspicions had been confirmed. "Just as I thought," he said, pulling out his prescription pad.

Medicine, ugh. Ramona's twitching stopped. Her nose and throat felt fine. "I feel much better," she assured the doctor as she eyed that prescription pad with distrust.

"An acute case of siblingitis. Not at all unusual around here, but it shouldn't last long." He tore off the prescription he had written, instructed Ramona to give it to her father, and hurried on down the hall.

Ramona could not remember the name of her illness. She tried to read the doctor's scribbly cursive writing, but she could not. She could only read neat cursive, the sort her teacher wrote on the blackboard.

Itching again, she was still staring at the slip of paper when Mr. Quimby and Beezus stepped out of the elevator. "Roberta is so tiny." Beezus was radiant with joy. "And she is perfectly darling. She has a little round nose and—oh, when you see her, you'll love her."

"I'm sick." Ramona tried to sound pitiful. "I've got something awful. A doctor said so."

Beezus paid no attention. "And Roberta has brown hair—"

Mr. Quimby interrupted. "What's this all about, Ramona?"

"A doctor said I had something, some kind of *itis,* and I have to have this right away." She handed her father her prescription and scratched one shoulder. "If I don't, I might get sicker."

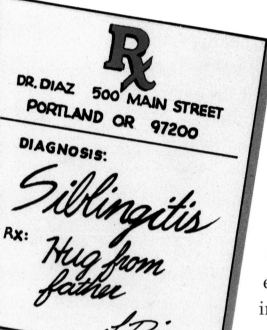

Mr. Quimby read the scribbly cursive, and then he did a strange thing. He lifted Ramona and gave her a big hug and a kiss, right there in the lobby. The itching stopped. Ramona felt much better. "You have acute siblingitis," explained her father. "*Itis* means inflammation."

Ramona already knew the meaning of sibling. Since her father had studied to be a teacher, brothers and sisters had become siblings to him.

"He understood you were worried and angry because you weren't allowed to see your new sibling, and prescribed attention," explained Mr. Quimby. "Now let's all go buy ice-cream cones before I fall asleep standing up."

Beezus said Roberta was too darling to be called a dumb word like sibling. Ramona felt silly, but she also felt better.

For the next three nights, Ramona took a book to the hospital and sat in the lobby, not reading, but sulking about the injustice of having to wait to see the strange new Roberta.

On the fourth day, Mr. Quimby took an hour off from the Shop-rite Market, picked up Beezus and Ramona, who were waiting in clean clothes, and drove to the hospital to bring home his wife and new daughter.

Ramona moved closer to Beezus when she saw her mother, holding a pink bundle, emerge from the elevator in a wheelchair pushed by a nurse and followed by Mr. Quimby carrying her bag. "Can't Mother walk?" she whispered.

"Of course she can walk," answered Beezus. "The hospital wants to make sure people get out without falling down and suing for a million dollars."

Mrs. Quimby waved to the girls. Roberta's face was hidden by a corner of a pink blanket, but the nurse had no time for a little girl eager to see a new baby. She pushed the wheelchair through the automatic door to the waiting car.

"*Now* can I see her?" begged Ramona when her

mother and Roberta were settled in the front, and the girls had climbed into the backseat.

"Dear Heart, of course you may." Mrs. Quimby then spoke the most beautiful words Ramona had ever heard, "Oh, Ramona, how I've missed you," as she turned back the blanket.

Ramona, leaning over the front seat for her first glimpse of the new baby sister, tried to hold her breath so she wouldn't breathe germs on Roberta, who did not look at all like the picture on the cover of *A Name for Your Baby*. Her face was bright pink, almost red, and her hair, unlike the smooth pale hair of the baby on the cover of the pamphlet, was dark and wild. Ramona did not know what to say. She did not feel that words like darling or adorable fitted this baby.

"She looks exactly like you looked when you were born," Mrs. Quimby told Ramona.

"She does?" Ramona found this hard to believe. She could not imagine that she had once looked like this red, frowning little creature.

"Well, what do you think of your new sister?" asked Mr. Quimby.

"She's so—so *little*," Ramona answered truthfully. Roberta opened her blue gray eyes.

"Mother!" cried Ramona. "She's cross-eyed."

Mrs. Quimby laughed. "All babies look cross-eyed sometimes. They outgrow it when they learn to focus." Sure enough, Roberta's eyes straightened out for a moment and then crossed again. She worked her mouth as if she didn't know what to do with it. She made little snuffling noises and lifted one arm as if she didn't know what it was for. "Why does her nightie have those little pockets at the ends of the sleeves?" asked Ramona. "They cover up her hands."

"They keep her from scratching herself," explained Mrs. Quimby. "She's too little to understand that fingernails scratch."

Ramona sat back and buckled her seat belt. She had once looked like Roberta. Amazing! She had once been that tiny, but she had grown, her hair had calmed down when she remembered to comb it, and she had learned to use her eyes and hands. "You know what I think?" she asked and did not wait for an answer. "I think it is hard work to be a baby." Ramona spoke as if she had discovered something unknown to the rest of the world. With her words came unexpected love and sympathy for the tiny person in her mother's arms.

"I hadn't thought of it that way," said Mrs. Quimby, "but I think you're right."

"Growing up is hard work," said Mr. Quimby as he drove away from the hospital. "Sometimes being grown-up is hard work."

"I know," said Ramona and thought some more. She thought about loose teeth, real sore throats, quarrels, misunderstandings with her teachers, longing for a bicycle her family could not afford, worrying when her parents bickered, how terrible she had felt when she hurt Beezus's feelings without meaning to, and all the long afternoons when Mrs. Kemp looked after her until her mother came from work. She had survived it all. "Isn't it funny?" she remarked as her father steered the car into their driveway.

"Isn't what funny?" asked her mother.

"That I used to be little and funny-looking and cross-eyed like Roberta," said Ramona. "And now look at me. I'm wonderful me!"

"Except when you're blunderful you," said Beezus.

Ramona did not mind when her family, except Roberta, who was too little, laughed. "Yup, wonderful, blunderful me," she said and was happy. She was winning at growing up.

MEET
BEVERLY
CLEARY

In a tiny library, a small girl sat on a shabby leather chair and learned something amazing. "I made the most magic of discoveries. There were books for children!" she remembers. Soon after, that girl, Beverly Cleary, was reading all the children's books she could find.

Beverly Cleary didn't like every book she read. She found that some books were boring. She thought, "Why couldn't authors skip all that tiresome description and write books in which something happened on every page?"

When she was in the third grade, her school librarian gave her an idea. She could write books herself! Beverly Cleary recalls, "I wanted to read funny stories about the sort of children I knew and I decided that someday when I grew up I would write them."

Her chance came when she married and moved into a new house. In a closet, Cleary found stacks of typing paper. "Now I'll have to write a book," she told her husband. She began a story about a boy and a dog on a bus.

Children all over the world now know about Henry Huggins and his dog, Ribsy. They also know and love Ramona Quimby, who appears in a series of eight books. Two of these books, *Ramona Quimby, Age 8* and *Ramona and Her Father,* have been named Newbery Honor Books. Among Beverly Cleary's many other popular titles are *Henry and Beezus, The Mouse and the Motorcycle,* and *Ralph S. Mouse.*

Don't Make At All

My mom says I'm her sugarplum.

My mom says I'm her lamb.

My mom says I'm completely perfect

Just the way I am.

My mom says I'm a super-special wonderful terrific

little guy.

My mom just had another baby.

Why?

Judith Viorst

On
GRANDDADDY'S
Farm

by Thomas B. Allen

*For Louise "Priss" McCallum
and
Dr. Benjamin Allen Shelton
In fond memory of
Granny and Granddaddy*

Over a bridge and down a tree-lined lane was Granddaddy's farm. It was there, in the rolling hills of middle Tennessee, that my cousins Priss and Ben Allen and I spent the summers.

Granddaddy was a brakeman for the L&N railroad and rode in the red caboose at the end of a long freight train. He worked the Nashville to Montgomery run and was away four days at a time.

Before he left the farm, he made sure that we three cousins knew what chores needed to be done while he was gone. We pumped water for the animals and weeded the vegetable garden. We fetched coal from the coal shed for Granny's stove and hauled water to the house from the dug well. Once we were entrusted with the job of hitching Old Mary, the big white draft horse, to the turning plow to cut a firebreak around the barn. A dry spell had left the ground so hard that one of us had to ride the plow to make it dig down into the packed earth.

Our little granny put in a full day baking and cooking, doing the wash, and taking care of the chickens and the garden. She also made sure that we cousins were well fed and well behaved and got our chores done.

After chores there was time
for fun. One day Ben Allen dared
me onto a yearling mule that had
never had anything on his back
before. When that mule felt me
there, he started bucking and
running around like crazy. I
whooped and hollered like a rodeo
rider as I hung on to his mane,
while Priss and Ben Allen laughed
till they cried. Granny, hearing
the ruckus, came rushing out of
the house. "Tom Burt, you get off
that mule right now!" she yelled.
The little mule gave one enormous
buck and flipped me right into a
thornbush.

The railroad yards weren't far from the farm, and
when Granddaddy's train came through the cut, headed
for home, the engineer gave a long pull on the whistle
cord, followed by three shorts, to let the families know
they were back. We knew it wouldn't be long before
Granddaddy would be coming down the lane, his empty
dinner basket riding lightly on his arm.

My cousins and I ran to meet him at the gate.
Granny stood on the front porch, smiling and wiping

her hands on her apron as if to say, "Yes, we're still here and everything's just fine."

After supper Granny and Granddaddy settled into their rockers on the porch to talk and enjoy the soft summer evening. Priss, Ben Allen, and I played outside till dark, shooting a scuffed-up basketball at the peach basket nailed above the car-shed door. We hoped Granny wouldn't tell about the yearling mule or any other trouble we'd gotten into.

We woke up every morning before dawn to the smell of biscuits baking and bacon frying. After a big breakfast we'd report to Granddaddy to get the day's assignment. I liked it best when it was a big job that needed doing, like bringing in the hay. It seemed more important than just doing chores.

After the hay was mowed and raked into windrows, we cousins piled it into stacks that Granddaddy tossed onto the wagon with one swoop of his pitchfork. It was hot work. Granny made several trips to the fields with a bucket of cool well water to quench our thirst. She always had something kind to say about our good work.

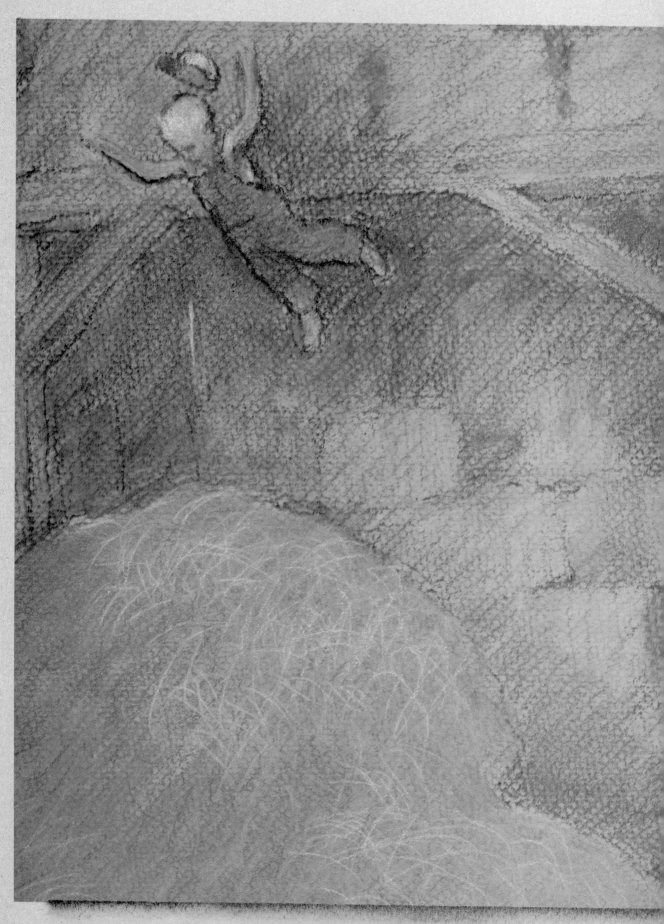

But for Priss, Ben Allen, and me the best part came after the hay was baled and stacked in the hayloft. We built a tunnel with the hay bales that we crawled through and then jumped from the loft into the straw piled below, again and again. We got covered with hay dust inside and out, but we did it anyway. The fun was worth the itching and sneezing.

Then Granny gave us a bar of fresh-smelling homemade soap to take down to the "blue hole" in Mill Creek. We hung our clothes on a tree limb and swam the dirt and dust away.

Sunday was the one day of the week when no work was done on Granddaddy's farm. After church more cousins and aunts and uncles came for Sunday dinner. All the cousins played baseball before dinner and took turns cranking the ice cream freezer. No matter how much ham and chicken and beans and potatoes and biscuits and tomatoes we ate, there was always room for homemade ice cream and Aunt Ruth's angel food cake.

Late in the afternoon the aunts and uncles and all the other cousins said their good-byes and drove off with everybody waving until the cars were out of sight. Half filled with excitement but half empty too, Priss, Ben Allen, and I looked for something to do to help level out those feelings. We went out behind the smokehouse to the horseshoe pits, where the uncles had just been, and pitched the rusty horseshoes that had once belonged to Old Mary.

Granddaddy liked to attend the Sunday evening church service, too, and he always invited us cousins to go with him. We hitched Old Mary to the buggy, and with a "come up" and a light slap of the reins, we were off at a trot. The church was small and plain. The benches were hard and had no backs. Granddaddy sat like a rock, listening to the words of the preacher, while we shifted and squirmed, trying to get comfortable. We were sound asleep by the time Old Mary trotted us back through the gate and up to the buggy shed.

It seemed like Granddaddy had just come home when he had to leave again for his run to Montgomery. Granny filled his basket with food for the journey. It was all homegrown or home-made: smoked ham, put-up vegetables, fresh fruit, biscuits, butter, blackberry jam, cake and pies. The basket weighed heavily on his arm as he told us cousins what chores needed to be done and reminded us to take care of Granny and the farm.

When we heard the train whistle blow, we knew that Grand-daddy had swung up onto the steps of his caboose. We could hear the train move out of the yards and through the cut, the choo-choo-choo of the steam engine and the click-clack, clickety-clack of the rails quickening and blending into the steady rhythm that was the heart-beat of Granddaddy's life on the railroad.

The sound of the train became more and more distant and, no matter how hard we listened, was gone. The empty silence that followed was slowly filled with the distant "bobwhite" call of quail, the buzzing of insects, and the clucking of chickens. Priss, Ben Allen, and I got right to our chores. There was water to be pumped, animals to be tended. We were proud to be taking care of Granddaddy's farm.

Thomas B. Allen

In *On Granddaddy's Farm,* Thomas B. Allen tells about the wonderful summers he spent with his cousins on his grandfather's farm in Tennessee. "The 1930s were simpler times, hard times," he says. "I wanted to show that, regardless of the lack of 'things,' children had fun and did their chores to help out, too."

Allen tells children who want to be writers, "Write about things you know about, are interested in, and . . . have experienced. Write with your own voice." In writing *On Granddaddy's Farm,* Allen followed his own advice.

Allen has illustrated many award-winning books by other writers, including *Blackberries in the Dark* and *In Coal Country,* but writing and illustrating his own story was a very special experience.

Aunt Molly, two cousins, my brother Jimmy, and me on the farm, 1930s

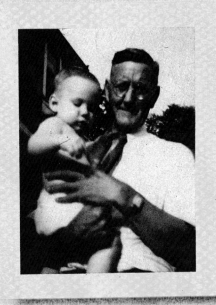

Granddaddy and me, 1929

In my studio in Carmel, New York, 1960s

My brother Jimmy (on the right) and me on the farm, 1930s

Under the Sunday Tree

They walk together

on Sundays

move slowly

through the park

always remembering

to stop awhile

at the place where

two trees arch as one

leaves touching

like family

Eloise Greenfield

Mr. Amos Ferguson's brightly colored folk-art painting shows a family group in the Bahamas. Eloise Greenfield wrote "Under the Sunday Tree" to go with Mr. Ferguson's painting.

Reading Resources

CONTENTS

JANUARY

	WED	THURS	FRI	SAT
TUES	1	2	3	4
7	8	9	10	11
14	15	16	17	18
21	22	23	24	25
28	29	30	31	

THURS	FRI	SAT
		1
6	7	8
13	14	21

THE LUNCHBOX

Plain ....
Mushroom ......
Peppers ......
Combination ...

Regular
4.00
4.50
4.50

Granola .....
Bagel .....
Muffin .....

1.25
.80

Bowl
Tomat

Nature Sala

IMPORTANT TELEPHONE NUMBERS

Ramona and Beezus's doctor 555-

Veterinarian 555-7943

Dad at work 555-4336

Aunt Bea and Uncle Hobart 5

Grandpa Day (818) 555-0

Mrs. Kemp 555-7329

Willa Jean 5

BOOK PARTS

SCIENCE AND YOU

By John M. Riley
Illustrated by
Marian Whalen

BETA PRESS • BOSTON

TITLE PAGE

Contents

TABLE OF CONTENTS

INDEX

INDEX PAGE

Calendar

1997

JANUARY

SUN	MON	TUES	WED	THURS	FRI	SAT
			1	2	3	4
5	6	7	8	9	10	11
12	13	14	15	16	17	18
19	20	21	22	23	24	25
26	27	28	29	30	31	

FEBRUARY

SUN	MON	TUES	WED	THURS	FRI	SAT
						1
2	3	4	5	6	7	8
9	10	11	12	13	14	15
16	17	18	19	20	21	22
23	24	25	26	27	28	

MARCH

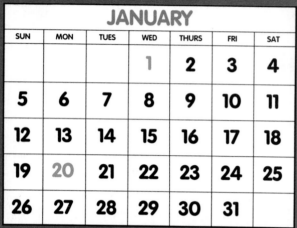

SUN	MON	TUES	WED	THURS	FRI	SAT
						1
2	3	4	5	6	7	8
9	10	11	12	13	14	15
16	17	18	19	20	21	22
23/30	24/31	25	26	27	28	29

APRIL

SUN	MON	TUES	WED	THURS	FRI	SAT
		1	2	3	4	5
6	7	8	9	10	11	12
13	14	15	16	17	18	19
20	21	22	23	24	25	26
27	28	29	30			

MAY

SUN	MON	TUES	WED	THURS	FRI	SAT
				1	2	3
4	5	6	7	8	9	10
11	12	13	14	15	16	17
18	19	20	21	22	23	24
25	26	27	28	29	30	31

JUNE

SUN	MON	TUES	WED	THURS	FRI	SAT
1	2	3	4	5	6	7
8	9	10	11	12	13	14
15	16	17	18	19	20	21
22	23	24	25	26	27	28
29	30					

CALENDAR

JULY

SUN	MON	TUES	WED	THURS	FRI	SAT
		1	2	3	4	5
6	7	8	9	10	11	12
13	14	15	16	17	18	19
20	21	22	23	24	25	26
27	28	29	30	31		

AUGUST

SUN	MON	TUES	WED	THURS	FRI	SAT
					1	2
3	4	5	6	7	8	9
10	11	12	13	14	15	16
17	18	19	20	21	22	23
24/31	25	26	27	28	29	30

SEPTEMBER

SUN	MON	TUES	WED	THURS	FRI	SAT
	1	2	3	4	5	6
7	8	9	10	11	12	13
14	15	16	17	18	19	20
21	22	23	24	25	26	27
28	29	30				

OCTOBER

SUN	MON	TUES	WED	THURS	FRI	SAT
			1	2	3	4
5	6	7	8	9	10	11
12	13	14	15	16	17	18
19	20	21	22	23	24	25
26	27	28	29	30	31	

NOVEMBER

SUN	MON	TUES	WED	THURS	FRI	SAT
						1
2	3	4	5	6	7	8
9	10	11	12	13	14	15
16	17	18	19	20	21	22
23/30	24	25	26	27	28	29

DECEMBER

SUN	MON	TUES	WED	THURS	FRI	SAT
	1	2	3	4	5	6
7	8	9	10	11	12	13
14	15	16	17	18	19	20
21	22	23	24	25	26	27
28	29	30	31			

SEPARATION OF WHITE LIGHT INTO COLORS BY A PRISM

A ray of white light is separated into seven colors when it passes through a prism:

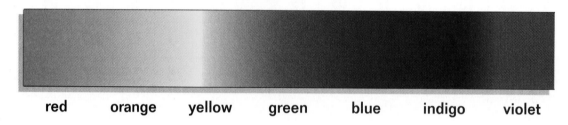

red   orange   yellow   green   blue   indigo   violet

HOW IT WORKS

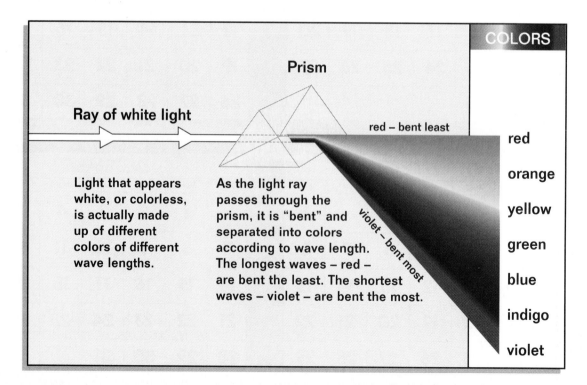

Prism

Ray of white light

red – bent least

violet – bent most

Light that appears white, or colorless, is actually made up of different colors of different wave lengths.

As the light ray passes through the prism, it is "bent" and separated into colors according to wave length. The longest waves – red – are bent the least. The shortest waves – violet – are bent the most.

COLORS

red

orange

yellow

green

blue

indigo

violet

HOW WE SEE

THE HUMAN EYE

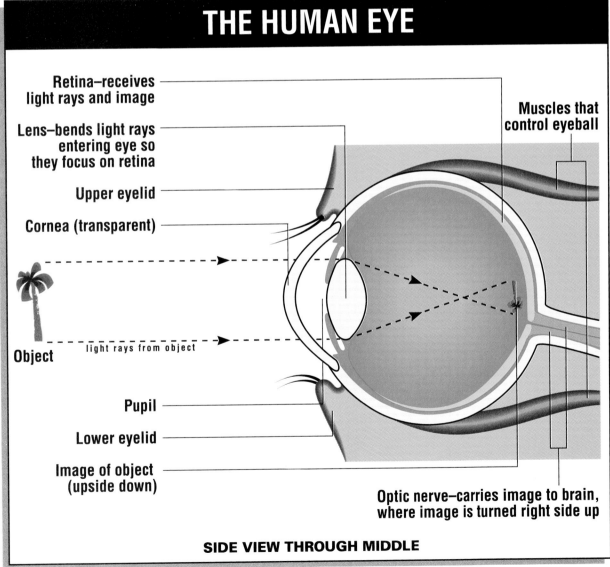

Retina–receives light rays and image

Lens–bends light rays entering eye so they focus on retina

Upper eyelid

Cornea (transparent)

Muscles that control eyeball

Object

light rays from object

Pupil

Lower eyelid

Image of object (upside down)

Optic nerve–carries image to brain, where image is turned right side up

SIDE VIEW THROUGH MIDDLE

Dictionary

main entry

definition

syllable division

pronunciation

part of speech

example sentence

homographs

moisten To make or become slightly wet. I *moistened* the soil around the plant.
mois·ten (moi′sən) *verb,* **moistened, moistening.**

moisture Water or other liquid in the air or on a surface; slight wetness. There was *moisture* on the window from the steam in the kitchen.
mois·ture (mois′chər) *noun.*

molar Any one of the large teeth at the back of the mouth. Molars have broad surfaces for grinding food.
mo·lar (mō′lər) *noun, plural* **molars.**

molasses A sweet, thick, yellowish brown syrup that is made from sugarcane.
mo·las·ses (mə las′iz) *noun.*

mold¹ A hollow form that is made in a special shape. A liquid or soft material is poured into a mold. When it hardens, it takes the shape of the mold. *Noun.*
—**1.** To make into a special shape; form. We *molded* the clay with our hands. **2.** To influence and give form to. Our parents help *mold* our habits. *Verb.*
mold (mōld) *noun, plural* **molds;** *verb,* **molded, molding.**

mold² A furry-looking covering of fungus that grows on food and damp surfaces. *Noun.*
—To become covered with mold. The bread *molded* because it wasn't refrigerated. *Verb.*
mold (mōld) *noun, plural* **molds;** *verb,* **molded, molding.**

molding A strip of wood, plaster, or other material that is used along the edges of walls, windows, or doorways for decoration.
mold·ing (mōl′ding) *noun, plural* **moldings.**

mole¹ A small, often raised, brown spot on the skin.
mole (mōl) *noun, plural* **moles.**

mole² A small animal with very soft, grayish fur that burrows holes underground. Moles have long claws and very small eyes.
mole (mōl) *noun, plural* **moles.**

mole²

472

molecule The smallest particle into which a substance can be divided without being changed chemically. For example, a molecule of water has two atoms of hydrogen and one atom of oxygen.
mol·e·cule (mol′ə kūl′) *noun, plural* **molecules.**

mollusk Any of a group of animals without backbones that usually have a soft body protected by a hard shell. Mollusks often live in or near water. Clams, snails, and oysters are mollusks.
mol·lusk (mol′əsk) *noun, plural* **mollusks.**

molt To shed the hair, feathers, skin, or shell and grow a new covering. Birds and snakes molt.
molt (mōlt) *verb,* **molted, molting.**

molten Melted by heat. Lava from a volcano is *molten* rock.
mol·ten (mōl′tən) *adjective.*

mom Mother. I call my mother *Mom.*
mom (mom) *noun, plural* **moms.**

moment **1.** A short period of time. I'll answer your question in just a *moment.* **2.** A particular point in time. Please come home the *moment* I call you or your dinner will get cold.
mo·ment (mō′mənt) *noun, plural* **moments.**

momentary Lasting only a short time. There was a *momentary* lull in the storm and then it rained heavily again.
mo·men·tar·y (mō′mən ter′ē) *adjective.*

momentous Having great importance. The end of the war was a *momentous* event for all.
mo·men·tous (mō men′təs) *adjective.*

momentum The force or speed that an object has when it is moving. A rock gains *momentum* as it rolls down a hill.
mo·men·tum (mō men′təm) *noun, plural* **momentums.**

Mon. An abbreviation for *Monday.*

monarch **1.** A king, queen, or other ruler of a state or country. **2.** A large orange and black butterfly found in North America.
mon·arch (mon′ərk) *noun, plural* **monarchs.**

monarchy **1.** Government by a king, queen, or other monarch. **2.** A nation or state that is ruled by a monarch.
mon·ar·chy (mon′ər kē) *noun, plural* **monarchies.**

monastery A place where monks live and work together.
mon·as·ter·y (mon′ə ster′ē) *noun, plural* **monasteries.**

word history

guide words

plural

illustration

compound word

M

verb forms

pronunciation key

Monday   The second day of the week.
Mon·day (mun′dē *or* mun′dā) *noun, plural* **Mondays.**

Word History

The Romans dedicated the second day of the week to the moon. This name was translated as an Old English word meaning "moon's day," or **Monday** as it became in modern English.

monetary   Of, in, or having to do with money or currency. This vase has great *monetary* value. The dollar is the *monetary* unit of the United States.
mon·e·tar·y (mon′i ter′ē) *adjective.*

money   The coins and paper currency of a country. Money is used to buy goods and pay people for services. Nickels, dimes, and dollar bills are money.
mon·ey (mun′ē) *noun, plural* **moneys.**

Mongolia   A country in central Asia.
Mon·go·li·a (mong gō′lē ə) *noun.*

mongoose   A slender animal that has a pointed face, a long tail, and rough, shaggy fur. Mongooses live in Africa and Asia. They eat rats and mice and are very quick.
mon·goose (mong′güs′) *noun, plural* **mongooses.**

mongoose

mongrel   An animal, especially a dog, or a plant that is a mixture of breeds.
mon·grel (mung′grəl *or* mong′grəl) *noun, plural* **mongrels.**

monitor   **1.** A student who is given a special duty to do. Some monitors help take attendance and others help keep order.   **2.** Any person who warns or keeps watch. The sailor's job was to be *monitor* of the radar screen.   **3.** The screen that a computer uses to display numbers, letters, and pictures. It is similar to a television screen. *Noun.*
—To watch over or observe something. Our teacher *monitored* the fire drill. *Verb.*
mon·i·tor (mon′i tər) *noun, plural* **monitors;** *verb,* **monitored, monitoring.**

monk   A man who has joined a religious order, lives in a monastery, and is bound by religious vows.
monk (mungk) *noun, plural* **monks.**

monkey   **1.** Any of a group of intelligent, furry animals with long tails and hands and feet that can grasp things. Most monkeys live in trees in tropical areas of the world. Monkeys are primates.   **2.** A playful or naughty child. *Noun.*
—To fool or play around in a mischievous way. The lifeguard asked us to quit *monkeying* around in the water. Don't *monkey* with the stove or you might get burned. *Verb.*
mon·key (mung′kē) *noun, plural* **monkeys;** *verb,* **monkeyed, monkeying.**

monkey

monkey wrench   A wrench with a jaw that can be adjusted to fit different sizes of nuts and bolts.

monogram   A design made by combining two or more initials of a person's name. You see monograms on such things as clothing, towels, and stationery.
mon·o·gram (mon′ə gram′) *noun, plural* **monograms.**

monologue   **1.** A long dramatic or comic speech or performance given by one person. The audience wept during the actor's *monologue* in the second act of the play.   **2.** A long speech made by one person who is part of a group.
mon·o·logue (mon′ə lôg′ *or* mon′ə log′) *noun, plural* **monologues.**

monopolize   **1.** To get or have a monopoly of.   **2.** To get, have, or use all of. Don't *monopolize* the teacher's attention.
mo·nop·o·lize (mə nop′ə līz′) *verb,* **monopolized, monopolizing.**

monopoly   **1.** The sole control of a product or service by a person or company. That bus

at; āpe; fär; câre; end; mē; it; īce; pîerce; hot; ōld; sông, fôrk; oil; out; up; ūse; rüle; půll; tûrn; chin; sing; shop; thin; **this;** hw in white; zh in treasure. The symbol ə stands for the unstressed vowel sound in about, taken, pencil, lemon, and circus.

473

Directions

ROCK PAINTING

Have you ever thought of painting on something besides paper? Try rocks! Use them as paperweights, door stops, or just to decorate a shelf or windowsill.

YOU WILL NEED

- smooth rocks of all shapes and sizes
- soap
- newspaper
- poster paints
- paintbrushes
- pencil
- felt-tip markers
- shellac (optional)

STEPS

1. Decide what type of rock painting you want to make.

2. Choose a rock. Wash it with soap and water. Let it dry overnight.

3. Place your rock on a piece of newspaper. Paint the whole rock with one color. Let it dry.

4. Use a pencil lightly to sketch your idea on the rock. Use different-colored paints or felt-tip markers to color it in. Let it dry.

5. (Optional) Coat your rock with shellac to make it shiny.

PASS IT ON!

In the "Pass It On" game, players whisper a secret message around a circle. But sometimes funny things happen when people speak and listen.

How to Play

1. Form a circle of four or more players.

2. The first player thinks of a short message. He or she whispers the message to the player on the right.

3. That player whispers the message to the next player on the right. Continue until the last player has heard the message.

4. The last player says the message aloud.

5. The first player tells if the message was correct.

Outcomes

1. If the message was correct, congratulate yourselves. Each player pats on the back the player to his or her right.

2. If the message was incorrect, investigate! Each player states aloud the message as he or she heard it to discover the place or places where it changed.

Rules

Instant Replay:

To hear the message repeated, each player may ask for an *instant replay* once.

Speak Clearly, Listen Carefully:

All players must try to communicate as best they can.

There was a line at the store.

There was a lion at this door?

Encyclopedia

RAILROADS

entry word

RAILROADS May 10, 1869, was an important day in the history of the United States. On that day a spike was driven that joined a railroad being built westward from Omaha, Neb., with a railroad being built eastward from Sacramento, Calif. The two roads were the Union Pacific and the Central Pacific. They met near Ogden, Utah. For the first time it was possible to travel by railroad all the way across the country.

Railroads now form a great network over the United States. In all, there are about 225,000 miles of them—just about enough to go to the moon. The country's railroads have had a great deal to do with building it into a strong nation.

It is easy to see how railroads got their name. They are truly roads built of rails. Standard rails are made of steel and are in sections 39 feet long. In most tracks heavy spikes are used to fasten the rails securely to wooden crossties. The ties are laid on beds of crushed rock, cinders, or gravel. Water can run off easily, and the ties stay firmly in place. Some of the newer tracks use rails welded into long lengths of half a mile or so—in some cases several miles. Another way newer tracks may be different is in the ties. Instead of being made of wood, they may be concrete. In Europe many tracks have steel ties.

The distance of the two rails from each other in a railroad track is called the gauge. Standard gauge is 4 feet, 8½ inches. Most

tracks in the United States are built on this gauge. It is possible for cars and engines of one railroad company to run on the tracks of other companies.

Many railroad tracks are double. One track is for trains going in one direction, and the other is for trains going in the other direction. If there is only one track, there must be sidings every so often. When two trains are approaching each other, one of the trains pulls off on a siding to let the other one pass.

Railroad companies build their tracks as nearly level and straight as they can. They avoid sharp corners and steep slopes. If a track must bend, it is laid in a big curve. If a mountain is in the way, the track may wind up and over it, or a tunnel may be dug through it. Bridges carry tracks over swamps, lakes, and rivers.

Passenger trains are not as common as they once were, but they are still an important way of carrying people from place to place. More than 300 million passengers a year ride on passenger trains in the United States. Carrying freight is an even more important work of railroads. The freight carried by American railroads amounts to more than a billion tons a year.

To carry their passengers and freight, railroads use many kinds of cars. On passenger trains we find coaches; diners; sleepers of several kinds; observation, or lounge, cars; and baggage cars. Some lines have dome cars. Among the many kinds of freight cars are tank cars, flatcars, boxcars, stockcars, refrigerator cars, and gondolas and hopper cars. Many freight cars have special fittings for carrying a particular kind of goods.

Much freight today travels piggyback on flatcars. Loaded truck trailers are put on the flatcars and then taken off the cars at the right city. The freight can be truck delivered at the exact spot where it is wanted. Another way freight is now handled is in containers of a standard size for travel by air, truck, ship, or train. The containers

The Meeting of Railroads of East and West

RAILROADS 1163

guide word

are quickly and easily transferred from one travel system to another.

Locomotives of different kinds pull the trains. Most of them are diesel-electric locomotives. Others are electric. Once steam locomotives were common, but over most of the world steam is no longer used.

It takes more than half a million people in the United States to keep the country's railroads running. In addition to the train crews themselves, there must be many workers in the railway yards, the repair shops, and the railway stations.

With so many trains on the railroads, there must be good signal systems to prevent wrecks and keep the trains on schedule. Many different ways of signaling are in use. They range from long-established ways such as semaphores and colored lights to completely automatic electronic control systems. In some cases no crew is needed.

One of the most remarkable things about railroads is how fast they developed. One does not have to go very far back beyond the day the two roads met in Utah to find the very beginning of railroads. Their ancestors were roads of wooden rails over which, in the early 1600's, horses pulled coal cars away from English coal mines. But the modern railroad goes back only to 1825, when the Stockton and Darlington Railway was built in England. The first American railroad built for carrying both freight and passengers was the Baltimore and Ohio. It was started in 1827, but not till several years later did good steam locomotives make regular service satisfactory. How strange a train of those days, with its passenger cars like stagecoaches, would look beside a modern train!

Though railroads are not as important as they were before the days of automobiles, buses, trucks, and airplanes, they are still often the best way of moving things on land. Trains can travel in almost any kind of weather and carry any kind of goods. (See BRIDGES; LOCOMOTIVE; SUBWAY; SIGNALING; TUNNELS.)

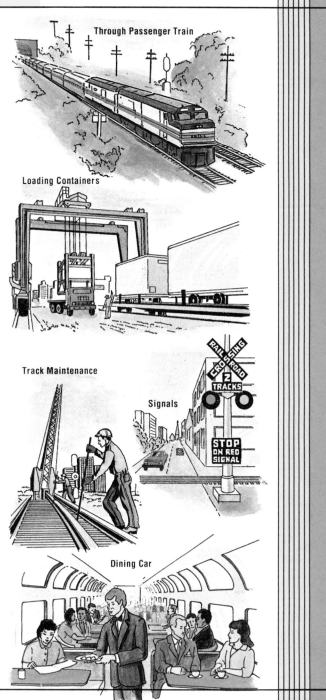

Through Passenger Train

Loading Containers

Track Maintenance

Signals

RAILROAD CROSSING 2 TRACKS

STOP ON RED SIGNAL

Dining Car

cross-references

Guidebooks

A Young Person's Guide to Trees

343

Horse Chestnut
height 80–100 feet, page 62

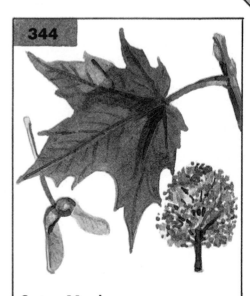

344

Sugar Maple
height 75–100 feet, page 75

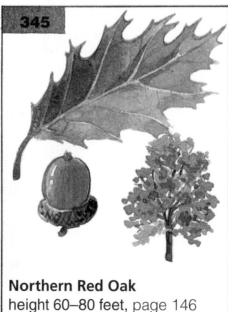

345

Northern Red Oak
height 60–80 feet, page 146

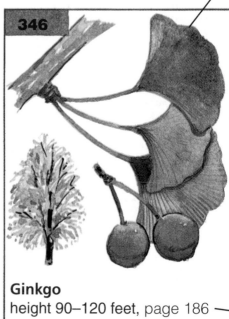

346

Ginkgo
height 90–120 feet, page 186

A Young Person's Guide to Trees

346 Ginkgo (also Gingko); Chinese Maidenhair Tree
Native to China, the ginkgo is now planted in mild climates worldwide, including the United States.

DESCRIPTION

Tree type: The ginkgo is a deciduous tree, which means that its leaves drop off in the fall. It is also a coniferous tree, because its seed is not covered by a true fruit or nut. (Most conifer seeds are produced in cones, like the familiar pine cone.)

Leaves: Ginkgo leaves are a rich green in spring, and turn bright yellow before dropping off in the fall. They measure 2–3 inches across and are fan-shaped. The upper edge is toothed, and each leaf is divided into two sections.

Seed: The sweet oval nut at the center is about ¾ inch long. The fruit is covered by an orange-yellow outer layer and gives off an unpleasant odor.

Height: 90–120 feet

Trunk: A ginkgo can measure more than 30 feet around.

Comments: The ginkgo dates from the time of the early dinosaurs (about 225 million years ago). Ginkgo fossils from these ancient times have been found in China. (The roasted white nut of the ginkgo is still a favorite food in China.) The ginkgo was brought to Japan and Korea many centuries ago. Later, in the 18th century, it was brought first to Europe and then to North America.

186

Maps

One tool scientists can use to explore and map the seafloor is the **multibeam sonar system.** Using this system, scientists send sound waves from the ocean's surface to the seafloor. There, the waves bump into different formations.

The different sizes and shapes of the formations cause the waves to bounce back to the ship at different times and from different directions. A computer uses this sound-wave information to show what the seafloor looks like.

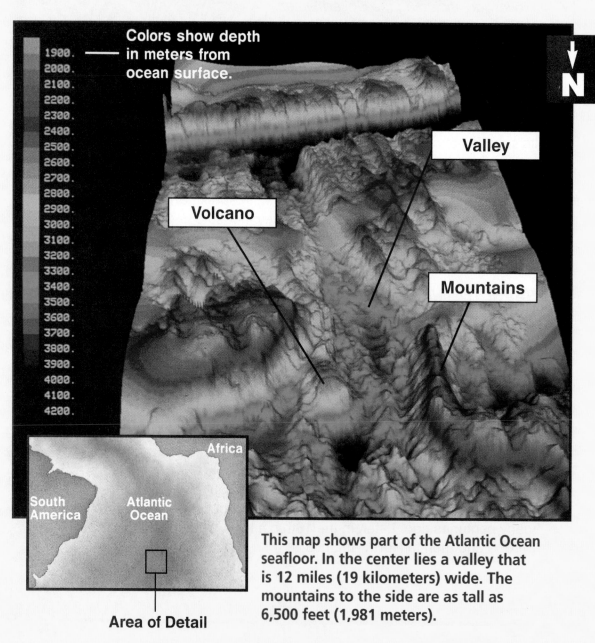

Colors show depth in meters from ocean surface.

1900.
2000.
2100.
2200.
2300.
2400.
2500.
2600.
2700.
2800.
2900.
3000.
3100.
3200.
3300.
3400.
3500.
3600.
3700.
3800.
3900.
4000.
4100.
4200.

N

Valley

Volcano

Mountains

Africa

South America

Atlantic Ocean

Area of Detail

This map shows part of the Atlantic Ocean seafloor. In the center lies a valley that is 12 miles (19 kilometers) wide. The mountains to the side are as tall as 6,500 feet (1,981 meters).

FLOOR PLAN OF KITCHEN

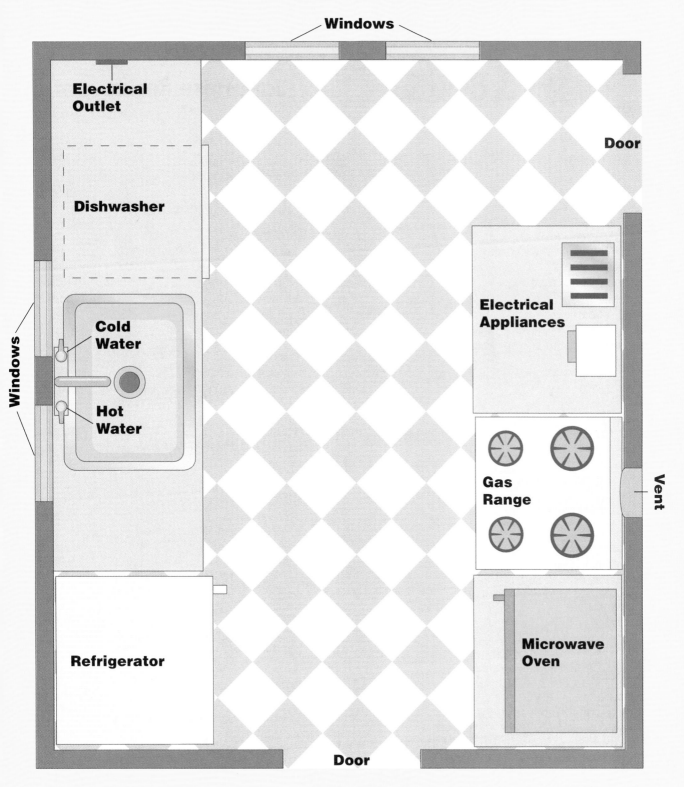

Windows

Electrical
Outlet

Dishwasher

Cold
Water

Hot
Water

Windows

Refrigerator

Door

Electrical
Appliances

Gas
Range

Vent

Microwave
Oven

Door

SHIGARAKI
Japanese Restaurant

APPETIZERS

Yakitori 3.25
*Broiled chunks of chicken on
skewer served with teriyaki sauce*

Beef Negimaki 4.75
*Thinly sliced broiled beef rolled with
scallions served with teriyaki sauce*

Gyoza 3.25
Fried shrimp dumplings

Age Tofu 3.25
Fried bean curd

Broiled Squid 3.50
With ginger sauce

SOUPS AND SALADS

Miso Soup 1.25
Soy bean soup

Sui Mono 1.25
Clear soup

Green Salad 2.25
Served with Japanese salad dressing

Seaweed Salad 4.95
Marinated seaweed

UDON

Nabe Yaki Udon 7.95
*Noodles with shrimp, chicken,
vegetables, and egg cooked
in stew style*

Beef Udon 6.50
Noodles with sliced beef in soup

ENTREES

Tempura
*Choice of shrimp, vegetables, or fish
deep fried in light batter with sauce
on the side*

Shrimp Tempura 9.95
Shrimp only

Vegetable Tempura 7.50
Assorted vegetables

Fish Tempura 8.50
Fish and vegetables

Teriyaki
*Choice of meat or fish (grilled),
in teriyaki sauce*

Beef Steak Teriyaki 11.95

Chicken Teriyaki 8.95

Swordfish Teriyaki 11.95

Shrimp Teriyaki 9.95

Nabe Mono

Sukiyaki 9.95
*Sliced beef, vegetables, and
tofu with sukiyaki sauce cooked
in stew style*

Yosen Nabe 10.95
*Assorted seafood and vegetables
cooked in broth*

SUSHI

Chirashi Sushi 9.95
*Assorted sliced raw fish on
a bed of seasoned rice*

Sashimi 9.95
*Thinly sliced assorted raw fish
served with green mustard and
soy sauce*

Tekka Maki 9.00
*Three rolls of raw tuna wrapped
in seasoned rice and seaweed*

DESSERTS

Ice Cream 2.00
Red bean, green tea, or ginger

Yokan 1.50
Red bean cake

THE LUNCHBOX

PIZZA POWER

	Small	Regular
Plain	2.75	4.00
Mushroom	3.00	4.50
Peppers	3.00	4.50
Combination	4.25	5.75

ALL SOUPED UP

	Bowl	Cup
Tomato	1.50	1.25
Bean	1.50	1.25
Chicken Noodle	1.75	1.50

WHAT'S SPECIAL?

Nature Salad: lettuce, tomato, green beans, house dressing	5.50
Turkey Burger: served with baked tortilla chips	4.50
Lemon Chicken: served with brown rice and steamed carrots	6.25

ENERGY SNACKS

Granola	1.25
Bagel	.80
Muffin	.95

WAY COOL

	Cone	Cup
Sherbet	1.00	1.25
Frozen Yogurt	1.25	2.50
Fruit Salad	1.75	

Extras .25
raisins
nuts
sprinkles

THIRST QUENCHERS

	Small	Large
Milk	.75	1.25
Herbal Teas	.75	
Fresh Juices	1.25	2.00

Apple, orange, grapefruit, cranberry, mango, papaya, carrot

Telephone Directory

For Emergency Calls Only

Fire and Rescue

Police Sheriff Highway Patrol

Ambulance

Coast Guard Search and Rescue

9-1-1

LISTINGS FOR EMERGENCY AGENCIES ARE CONTINUED ON PAGE A2

For Non-Emergency Calls please use the appropriate 7-digit number.

Telephone numbers for City, County, State, and Federal agencies are listed in the White Pages.

Write in local number here:

Doctor _____

Telecommunications Device for the Deaf (TDD) Emergency Calls:

*Dial 9-1-1

*Press the Space Bar Until Someone Answers.

En una emergencia la forma más rápida de obtener auxilio es marcar 9-1-1

Notice!

Dialing 9-1-1 and Your Privacy
When reporting an emergency by dialing 9-1-1, your number (including non-published number) and address may be automatically displayed on a viewing screen. This information enables the emergency agency to quickly locate you if the call is interrupted.

If you do not wish to have your telephone number and address displayed, use the appropriate 7-digit emergency number.

EMERGENCY NUMBERS

128 PHOTO—POLLARD

Photo Phinishers 12 Beltway	555-4235
Phung Yan Chu 16 Center Ave	555-0971
PHYLLIS'S PET SHOP	
1166 Park Hwy	**555-8920**
Pichard Nell 18 Dysart Ave	555-9810
Pichard Roberto 9 Day St	555-9356
Pickett Ana 809 Buena Vista	555-0842
Picovsky Susan 62 Wood St	555-9854
Pidgeon C G 920 Main St	555-4845
Pie & Cake Co 622 Park Hwy	555-7590
Piedra Bill 51 Horace St	555-8592
Piedras M...Dysart Ave	555-4521
Pittman Gale 64 River St	555-9978
Pittman Roger MD	
1245 Santa Ana Blvd	555-9863
Pitts Loleta 133 Allen Way	555-8359
Pizel John 501 Whitney Ave	555-8252
PLAINVILLE BOAT SHOP	
1621 Park Hwy	**555-2769**
Plante Kevan 113 River St	555-7458
Plante Sylvia 113 River St	555-7460
Pletcher Arlen 75 Wood St	555-3148
Plumisto LeRoy 441 River St	555-2323
...a 2 Allen Way	...692

WHITE PAGES

IMPORTANT TELEPHONE NUMBERS

Hospital 555-0680

Fire Department 555-9823

Police 555-4626

Dentist 555-1572

School 555-5460

Library 555-8123

Mom's doctor 555-9589

Ramona and Beezus's doctor 555-4389

Veterinarian 555-7943

Dad at work 555-4336

Aunt Bea and Uncle Hobart 555-3701

Grandpa Day (818) 555-0197

Mrs. Kemp 555-7329

Howie and Willa Jean 555-9847

GLOS

This glossary can help you to pronounce and find out the meanings of words in this book that you may not know.

The words are listed in alphabetical order. Guide words at the top of each page tell you the first and last words on the page.

Each word is divided into syllables. The way to pronounce each word is given next. You can understand the pronunciation respelling by using the key at right. A shorter key appears at the bottom of every other page.

When a word has more than one syllable, a dark accent mark (′) shows which syllable is stressed. In some words, a light accent mark (′) shows which syllable has a less heavy stress.

Glossary entries are based on entries in *The Macmillan/McGraw-Hill School Dictionary 1.*

SARY

a	at, bad	**d**	dear, soda, bad
ā	ape, pain, day, break	**f**	five, defend, leaf, off, cough, elephant
ä	father, car, heart		
âr	care, pair, bear, their, where	**g**	game, ago, fog, egg
e	end, pet, said, heaven, friend	**h**	hat, ahead
ē	equal, me, feet, team, piece, key	**hw**	white, whether, which
i	it, big, English, hymn	**j**	joke, enjoy, gem, page, edge
ī	ice, fine, lie, my	**k**	kite, bakery, seek, tack, cat
îr	ear, deer, here, pierce	**l**	lid, sailor, feel, ball, allow
o	odd, hot, watch	**m**	man, family, dream
ō	old, oat, toe, low	**n**	not, final, pan, knife
ô	coffee, all, taught, law, fought	**ng**	long, singer, pink
ôr	order, fork, horse, story, pour	**p**	pail, repair, soap, happy
oi	oil, toy	**r**	ride, parent, wear, more, marry
ou	out, now	**s**	sit, aside, pets, cent, pass
u	up, mud, love, double	**sh**	shoe, washer, fish, mission, nation
ū	use, mule, cue, feud, few	**t**	tag, pretend, fat, button, dressed
ü	rule, true, food	**th**	thin, panther, both
u̇	put, wood, should	**th̲**	this, mother, smooth
ûr	burn, hurry, term, bird, word, courage	**v**	very, favor, wave
ə	about, taken, pencil, lemon, circus	**w**	wet, weather, reward
b	bat, above, job	**y**	yes, onion
ch	chin, such, match	**z**	zoo, lazy, jazz, rose, dogs, houses
		zh	vision, treasure, seizure

adobe A sandy kind of clay used to make bricks. Bits of straw are sometimes mixed with the clay, and the bricks are dried in the sun. Many buildings in Mexico and the southwestern United States are made of *adobe*.
    a•do•be (ə dō′bē) *noun, plural* **adobes.**

adobe

Aiko (ä ē′kō).

Algie (al′jē).

amaze To surprise greatly; astonish. The child's speed at solving mathematical problems *amazed* us.
    a•maze (ə māz′) *verb,* **amazed, amazing.**

angle The figure formed by two lines or flat surfaces that stretch out from one point or line.
    an•gle (ang′gəl) *noun, plural* **angles.**

announce To make something known in an official or formal way. The principal *announced* that the school would be closed because of the blizzard.
    an•nounce (ə nouns′) *verb,* **announced, announcing.**

anxiously In a nervous, worried, or fearful way. My cousin *anxiously* gripped the steering wheel as he drove on the slippery mountain roads.
    anx•ious•ly (angk′shəs lē) *adverb.*

aphid A small insect that lives by sucking juices from plants.
    a•phid (ā′ fid *or* af′id) *noun, plural* **aphids.**

ashamed **1.** Feeling shame; upset or guilty because one has done something wrong or silly. The student was *ashamed* for having failed the arithmetic test. **2.** Not wanting to do something because of fear or shame. I was *ashamed* to admit that I fell off my bicycle.
    a•shamed (ə shāmd′) *adjective.*

Atlantic Ocean An ocean separating Europe and Africa from North and South America.
    At•lan•tic O•cean (at lan′tik ō′shən).

bargain **1.** Something offered for sale or bought at a low price. At only ten cents, this ballpoint pen is a *bargain.* **2.** An agreement. We made a *bargain* that I would wash the dishes if you would dry them.
    bar•gain (bär′gin) *noun, plural* **bargains.**

batter[1] To hit over and over again with heavy blows. The sailor was afraid the high waves would *batter* the small boat to pieces.
bat•ter (bat'ər) *verb,* **battered, battering.**

batter[2] A mixture of flour, milk or water, and other things. *Batter* is fried or baked to make pancakes, biscuits, or cakes.
bat•ter (bat'ər) *noun, plural* **batters.**

batter[3] A person whose turn it is to hit the ball in a game of baseball or softball.
bat•ter (bat'ər) *noun, plural* **batters.**

beam A narrow ray of light. A *beam* of sunlight came through the window. *Noun.*
—To smile happily. The parents *beamed* with pride as their child gave a speech. *Verb.*
beam (bēm) *noun, plural* **beams;** *verb,* **beamed, beaming.**

beam

belief A feeling that something is true, real, or worthwhile. My *belief* in my country is strong.
be•lief (bi lēf') *noun, plural* **beliefs.**

brim An edge or rim. My glass is filled to the *brim.* That beach hat has a wide *brim.*
brim (brim) *noun, plural* **brims.**

C

cautious To do something with great care to avoid danger or risk. Always be *cautious* when you ride your bicycle.
cau•tious (kô'shəs) *adjective.*

challenge **1.** To question the truth or correctness of; doubt or dispute. They *challenged* my claim that bats are mammals. **2.** To ask to take part in a contest or fight. They *challenged* us to a race around the block. **3.** To make someone think, work, or try hard; make demands on. The puzzle *challenged* us all.
chal•lenge (chal'ənj) *verb,* **challenged, challenging.**

chore A small job or task. Feeding the chickens every morning was one of my *chores* on the farm.
chore (chôr) *noun, plural* **chores.**

Chou (jō).

clutch **1.** To grasp tightly. I *clutched* the money in my hand on the way to the grocery store. **2.** To try to grasp or seize. I *clutched* at the railing when I slipped on the stairs.
clutch (kluch) *verb,* **clutched, clutching.**

comfortable Giving ease or comfort. My own bed was so *comfortable* after our camping trip.
com•fort•a•ble (kum'fər tə bəl *or* kumf'tə bəl) *adjective.*

---

at; āpe; fär; câre; end; mē; it; īce; pîerce; hot; ōld; sông; fôrk; oil; out; up; ūse; rüle; půll; tûrn; chin; sing; shop; thin; <u>th</u>is; hw in white; zh in treasure. The symbol ə stands for the unstressed vowel sound in about, taken, pencil, lemon, and circus.

---

complain To say that something is wrong; find fault. The passengers *complained* that the train was never on time.
> **com•plain** (kəm plān′) *verb,* **complained, complaining.**

connect To fasten or join together. We had no trouble *connecting* the trailer to the car.
> **con•nect** (kə nekt′) *verb,* **connected, connecting.**

costume **1.** Clothes worn in order to look like someone or something else. I wore a clown *costume* in the school play. **2.** Clothes worn at a particular time or place or by particular people. My cousins collect dolls dressed in the national *costumes* of different countries.
> **cos•tume** (kos′tüm *or* kos′tūm) *noun, plural* **costumes.**

costumes

crooked Not straight; bent or curving. The path that we followed through the woods was very *crooked.*
> **crook•ed** (krůk′id) *adjective.*

crystal A body that is formed by certain substances when they change into a solid. Crystals have flat surfaces and a regular shape. Salt, sugar, and ice all form in *crystals.*
> **crys•tal** (kris′təl) *noun, plural* **crystals.**

crystals

cushion A pillow or soft pad used to sit, lie, or rest on. Our couch has three *cushions* on the seat. *Noun.*
—To soften a blow or shock. The pile of leaves *cushioned* my fall from the tree. *Verb.*
> **cush•ion** (kůsh′ən) *noun, plural* **cushions;** *verb,* **cushioned, cushioning.**

D

delicious Pleasing or delightful to the taste or smell. The stew cooking for dinner smelled *delicious.*
> **de•li•cious** (di lish′əs) *adjective.*

delight **1.** To give great pleasure or joy to; please very much. The puppet show *delighted* the children. **2.** To have or to take great pleasure. My grandparents *delight* in telling us stories about their childhood.
> **de•light** (di līt′) *verb,* **delighted, delighting.**

depart 1. To go away; leave. The train is due to *depart* from the station at ten o'clock. **2.** To change or differ. We *departed* from our usual routine and held class outdoors.
    de•part (di pärt') *verb,* **departed, departing.**

depth The distance from top to bottom or from front to back. The *depth* of the pool was 5 feet. The *depth* of our backyard is 50 feet.
    depth (depth) *noun, plural* **depths.**

difficult 1. Needing much effort; hard to do; not easy. This is a *difficult* arithmetic problem. **2.** Hard to get along with or please. Some people become *difficult* when they can't have their way.
    dif•fi•cult (dif'i kult') *adjective.*

directly At once; without delay. Please come home *directly* after the concert.
    di•rect•ly (di rekt'lē *or* dī rekt'lē) *adverb.*

disappear To go out of sight. We watched the sun *disappear* behind a cloud.
    dis•ap•pear (dis'ə pîr') *verb,* **disappeared, disappearing.**

disappointment The feeling a person has when hopes are not met. Roberta couldn't hide her *disappointment* when it rained and the picnic was called off.
    dis•ap•point•ment (dis'ə point'mənt) *noun, plural* **disappointments.**

discover 1. To notice; come upon. I *discovered* a spelling error in my report. **2.** To see or find out for the first time. The explorer was the first to *discover* the pass through the mountains.
    dis•cov•er (dis kuv'ər) *verb,* **discovered, discovering.**

disguise To change the way one looks in order to hide one's real identity or look like someone else. The children *disguised* themselves as pirates and monsters on Halloween. *Verb.*
—Something that changes or hides the way one looks. A mustache was part of a thief's *disguise. Noun.*
    dis•guise (dis gīz') *verb,* **disguised, disguising;** *noun, plural* **disguises.**

distant Far away in space or time; not near. The novel told of a family that had traveled to the United States from a *distant* country.
    dis•tant (dis'tənt) *adjective.*

eldest Born first; oldest. I am the *eldest* of three children.
    eld•est (el'dist) *adjective.*

encourage To give courage, hope, or confidence to; urge on. The coach *encouraged* the students to try out for the swimming team.
    en•cour•age (en kûr'ij) *verb,* **encouraged, encouraging.**

endanger 1. To threaten with becoming extinct. Pollution is *endangering* many species of animals. **2.** To put in a situation that is dangerous. The flood *endangered* the lives of many people.
    en•dan•ger (en dān'jər) *verb,* **endangered, endangering.**

at; āpe; fär; câre; end; mē; it; īce; pîerce; hot; ōld; sông; fôrk; oil; out; up; ūse; rüle; pùll; tûrn; chin; sing; shop; thin; this; hw in white; zh in treasure. The symbol ə stands for the unstressed vowel sound in about, taken, pencil, lemon, and circus.

engineer 1. A person who drives a locomotive. The *engineer* blew the train's whistle as it neared the station. **2.** A person who is trained in work that uses scientific knowledge for practical things, such as building dams, drilling for oil, producing plastics, or designing machines. An *engineer* may plan and design bridges, roads, or airplanes.
    en•gi•neer (en′jə nîr′) *noun*, *plural* **engineers.**

enormous Much greater than the usual size or amount; very large. Some dinosaurs were *enormous*.
    e•nor•mous (i nôr′məs) *adjective*.

enormous

entire Having all the parts; with nothing left out; whole. Did you eat the *entire* bowl of salad? It took an *entire* morning to clean the attic.
    en•tire (en tīr′) *adjective*.

equipment Anything that is provided for a particular purpose or use; supplies. The students bought a tent, sleeping bags, and other camping *equipment*.
    e•quip•ment (i kwip′mənt) *noun*.

Espino, Fernando (es pē′no, fûr nän′dō).

examine 1. To look at closely and carefully; check. We *examined* the baseball bat to be sure it wasn't cracked. **2.** To question in a careful way or test, usually to discover what a person knows. The lawyer *examined* the witness during the trial.
    ex•am•ine (eg zam′in) *verb*, **examined, examining.**

excitement The condition of being stirred up; aroused. We could hardly sleep because of our *excitement* about starting the trip tomorrow.
    ex•cite•ment (ek sīt′mənt) *noun*.

exhaust 1. To make very weak or tired. The long, hot hike *exhausted* us. **2.** To use up completely. The campers *exhausted* their supply of water, so they drank from a fresh spring.
    ex•haust (eg zôst′) *verb*, **exhausted, exhausting.**

exhibit Something shown. We went to see the *exhibit* of African art at the museum. The science *exhibit* won first prize.
    ex•hib•it (eg zib′it) *noun*, *plural* **exhibits.**

expect 1. To think; suppose. I *expect* I won't be going to school if I still have the flu tomorrow. **2.** To look forward to. I *expect* to see my grandparents at Thanksgiving. **3.** To want something because it is right or necessary. The teacher *expected* an apology from the rude child.
    ex•pect (ek spekt′) *verb*, **expected, expecting.**

experiment A test that is used to discover or prove something by watching results very carefully. The class did an *experiment* to show that a fire needs oxygen to burn.
ex•per•i•ment (ek sper′ə mənt) *noun, plural* **experiments.**

explorer A person who travels in unknown places for the purpose of discovery.
ex•plor•er (ek splôr′ər) *noun, plural* **explorers.**

F

fable 1. A made-up or untrue story. Have you heard the old *fable* that porcupines can shoot their quills? **2.** A story that is meant to teach a lesson. The characters in *fables* are often animals that talk and act like people.
fa•ble (fā′bəl) *noun, plural* **fables.**

fable

flow 1. To hang or fall loosely. When I was young, my hair *flowed* to my waist. **2.** To move along steadily in a stream. Water *flows* through these pipes.
flow (flō) *verb,* **flowed, flowing.**

foreign Outside a person's own country. Have you ever visited any *foreign* countries?
for•eign (fôr′ən) *adjective.*

freight Having to do with the carrying of goods by land, air, or water. This *freight* train carries wheat to the city. *Adjective.*
—The goods carried in this way; cargo. It took five hours to unload all the *freight* from the train. *Noun.*
freight (frāt) *adjective; noun.*

furious Very angry. My folks were *furious* when we missed the train by one minute.
fu•ri•ous (fyu̇r′ē əs) *adjective.*

G

glance To take a quick look. I *glanced* in the mirror.
glance (glans) *verb,* **glanced, glancing.**

gobble To eat something quickly and in large chunks. The hungry dog *gobbled* its food and then begged for more.
gob•ble (gob′əl) *verb,* **gobbled, gobbling.**

at; āpe; fär; câre; end; mē; it; īce; pîerce; hot; ōld; sông; fôrk; oil; out; up; ūse; rüle; pu̇ll; tûrn; chin; sing; shop; thin; <u>th</u>is; **hw** in **wh**ite; **zh** in treasure. The symbol ə stands for the unstressed vowel sound in about, taken, pencil, lemon, and circus.

government 1. The group of people in charge of ruling or managing a country, state, city, or other place. The *government* in this country is elected by the people. **2.** A way of ruling or governing. The Canadian people have a democratic *government*.

> **gov•ern•ment** (guv′ərn mənt *or* guv′ər mənt) *noun, plural* **governments.**

Gulf of Mexico An arm of the Atlantic between the United States and Mexico.

> **Gulf of Mex•i•co** (gulf uv mek′si kō′).

Gulf of Mexico

haul 1. To carry; transport. Railroads *haul* freight across the country.
2. To pull or move with force; drag. It took three of us to *haul* the heavy trunk up the stairs. *Verb.*
—The act of carrying or transporting. Give the rope a *haul*. *Noun.*
▲ Another word that sounds like this is **hall**.

> **haul** (hôl) *verb,* **hauled, hauling;** *noun, plural* **hauls.**

hei yo (hā′ yō′).

imaginary Existing only in the mind; not real. Even though they seem real, the characters and places in my favorite story are only *imaginary*.

> **i•mag•i•nar•y** (i maj′ə ner′ē) *adjective.*

interrupt 1. To break in upon or stop a person who is acting or speaking. Please do not *interrupt* me again when I'm talking. **2.** To stop for a time; break off. I *interrupted* my work to answer the telephone.

> **in•ter•rupt** (in′tə rupt′) *verb,* **interrupted, interrupting.**

interview A meeting in which someone obtains information. The magazine writer arranged for an *interview* with the scientist.

> **in•ter•view** (in′tər vū′) *noun, plural* **interviews.**

invent 1. To make or think of for the first time; create. Do you know who *invented* the phonograph? **2.** To make up. I am ashamed to admit I *invented* an excuse for being late.

> **in•vent** (in vent′) *verb,* **invented, inventing.**

Word History

The word **invent** comes from a Latin word meaning "to come upon" or "find." At first the word *invent* was used to describe the finding of an answer, the solution to a problem, or the means to do something. This use led to our modern meaning of the word *invent*, "to make or think of for the first time."

K

kaleidoscope A tube that contains mirrors and often small pieces of colored glass or other colored objects at one end. When the other end of the tube is held up to the eye and turned, the mirrors reflect a series of changing patterns.
ka•lei•do•scope (kə lī′də skōp′) *noun*, *plural* **kaleidoscopes.**

Word History

The word **kaleidoscope** comes from the Greek words *kalos,* meaning "beautiful," *eidos,* meaning "form," and *skopos* meaning "to look at." Together those words mean "to look at beautiful forms."

---

kimono A loose robe that is tied with a sash. *Kimonos* are worn by both men and women in Japan, usually on holidays or other special occasions.
ki•mo•no (ki mō′nə) *noun, plural* **kimonos.**

kimono

L

length The distance from one end to the other end. The *length* of a football field is 100 yards.
length (lengkth *or* length) *noun, plural* **lengths.**

Lon Po Po (lon pô pô *or* lōng bô bô).

M

magnify 1. To make something look bigger than it really is. The microscope *magnified* the cells one hundred times. **2.** To make something seem more important than it really is. Some people *magnify* their health problems.
mag•ni•fy (mag′nə fī′) *verb,* **magnified, magnifying.**

magnify

---

at; āpe; fär; câre; end; mē; it; īce; pîerce; hot; ōld; sông; fôrk; oil; out; up; ūse; rüle; pùll; tûrn; chin; sing; shop; thin; <u>th</u>is; hw in white; zh in treasure. The symbol ə stands for the unstressed vowel sound in about, taken, pencil, lemon, and circus.

---

material What something is made of or used for. My winter coat is made of heavy *material*.
    ma•te•ri•al (mə tîr′ē əl) *noun*, *plural* **materials.**

messenger A person who delivers messages or runs errands. A *messenger* brought the telegram to our house.
    mes•sen•ger (mes′ən jər) *noun*, *plural* **messengers.**

mischievous Playful. That *mischievous* child hid my slippers again.
    mis•chie•vous (mis′chə vəs) *adjective.*

miserable 1. Very unhappy; wretched. We all felt *miserable*. 2. Causing discomfort or unhappiness. I had a *miserable* cold.
    mis•er•a•ble (miz′ər ə bəl) *adjective.*

mist A cloud of tiny drops of water or other liquid in the air; fog. Early this morning, there was a heavy *mist* over the lake.
    mist (mist) *noun.*

mist

museum A building where objects of art, science, or history are kept and displayed for people to see.
    mu•se•um (mū zē′əm) *noun*, *plural* **museums.**

N

nervous 1. Fearful or timid. I am very *nervous* about taking the exam. 2. Not able to relax; tense. Loud noises make me *nervous*.
    nerv•ous (nûr′vəs) *adjective.*

O

opposite 1. On the other side of or across from another person or thing; facing. They live on the *opposite* side of the street from me. 2. Completely different. Hot is *opposite* to cold.
    op•po•site (op′ə zit) *adjective.*

P

pace To walk back and forth across. The tiger *paced* in its cage. *Verb.* —1. A single step. The soldiers took two *paces* forward. 2. The rate of speed in running or moving. We walked home at a fast *pace*. *Noun.*
    pace (pās) *verb*, **paced, pacing;** *noun*, *plural* **paces.**

Pacific Ocean An ocean bordered by North and South America on the east and by Asia and Australia on the west, the largest body of water in the world.
    Pa•ci•fic O•cean (pə sif′ik ō′shən).

Panama A country in Central America.

Panama

Paotze (pow′zuh).

peer **1.** To look hard or closely, as if trying to see something clearly. The scientist *peered* at the slide through a microscope. **2.** To come slightly into view. The sun *peered* over the mountain. ▲ Another word that sounds like this is **pier**.
    peer (pîr) *verb,* **peered, peering.**

Pepita (pe pē′tə).

permit To allow or let. My parents will not *permit* me to play outside after it is dark.
    per•mit (pər mit′) *verb,* **permitted, permitting.**

poinciana A tropical tree that has clusters of large red, yellow, or orange flowers.
    poin•ci•a•na (poin′sē an′ə) *noun.*

pollution Harmful materials such as certain gases, chemicals, and wastes that make the air, water, or soil dirty and impure. *Pollution* in the pond killed the fish that once lived there.
    pol•lu•tion (pə lü′shən) *noun.*

precious Having great value. Gold is a *precious* metal.
    pre•cious (presh′əs) *adjective.*

pressure **1.** Force caused by one thing pushing against another thing. The *pressure* of the driver's foot on the gas pedal made the car go faster. **2.** A burden; strain. They went camping to get away from the *pressure* of city life. *Noun.*
—To urge strongly. The salesperson tried to *pressure* people into buying things they didn't need. *Verb.*
    pres•sure (presh′ər) *noun, plural* **pressures;** *verb,* **pressured, pressuring.**

quarter **1.** One of four equal parts. We divided the apple pie into four *quarters* for dessert. **2.** One of the four equal time periods into which certain games are divided. Barbara scored the winning goal in the fourth *quarter.*
    quar•ter (kwôr′tər) *noun, plural* **quarters.**

at; āpe; fär; câre; end; mē; it; īce; pîerce; hot; ōld; sông; fôrk; oil; out; up; ūse; rüle; púll; tûrn; chin; sing; shop; thin; <u>th</u>is; hw in white; zh in treasure. The symbol ə stands for the unstressed vowel sound in about, taken, pencil, lemon, and circus.

R

rapid Very quick; fast. The train went at a *rapid* pace.
ra•pid (rap′id) *adjective.*

realize To understand completely. I didn't *realize* how late it was.
re•al•ize (rē′ə līz′) *verb,* **realized, realizing.**

recognize 1. To know and remember from before; identify. I didn't *recognize* you at first. **2.** To understand and accept as being true, right, or valid. We *recognize* that it was our duty to report the crime to the police.
re•cog•nize (rek′əg nīz′) *verb,* **recognized, recognizing.**

reflection An image given back by a surface such as a mirror or a pond. I looked at my *reflection* in the store window.
re•flec•tion (ri flek′shən) *noun,* *plural* **reflections.**

reflection

remains 1. Something that is left. The explorers found the *remains* of an ancient city. **2.** To stay behind in the same place. Our dog *remained* at home when we went to visit our grandfather.
re•mains (ri mānz′) *plural noun.*

remarkable Worthy of being noticed; not ordinary; unusual. Your science project is *remarkable.*
re•mark•a•ble (ri mär′kə bəl) *adjective.*

restaurant A place where food is prepared and served to customers. In many *restaurants* customers serve themselves.
res•tau•rant (res′tə rənt *or* res′tə ränt′) *noun, plural* **restaurants.**

Word History

The word **restaurant** comes from a French word meaning "to restore." At a *restaurant* people can sit down, eat, and feel refreshed, or "restored."

---

restless 1. Not able to be at ease or relax. We got *restless* because the speech was so long. **2.** Not giving rest. My sister spent a *restless* night before her piano recital.
rest•less (rest′lis) *adjective.*

rhythm A regular or orderly repeating of sounds or movements. We marched to the *rhythm* of drums beating steadily.
rhyth•m (rith′əm) *noun, plural* **rhythms.**

route A road or other course used for traveling. We drove along the ocean *route* for our trip to the beach. ▲ Another word that sounds like this is **root.**
route (rüt *or* rout) *noun, plural* **routes.**

S

Sabana Grande (sə ban′ə grän′dā).

Santa Marta (san′tə mär′tə).

scarcely Barely or hardly. I had *scarcely* come in when the phone rang. There was *scarcely* a person on the street.
> **scarce•ly** (skârs′lē) *adverb.*

scavenger An animal that feeds on carcasses or decaying plant matter.
> **scav•en•ger** (skav′ən jər) *noun, plural* **scavengers.**

section **1.** A part taken from the whole; portion. They planted vegetables in one *section* of the garden. **2.** A part of something written. I always read the sports *section* of a newspaper. **3.** A part of an area or group. The trumpet player plays in the brass *section* of the orchestra.
> **sec•tion** (sek′shən) *noun, plural* **sections.**

section

Señor Remon (sen yôr′ rə môn′).

Señora Alfaro (sen yôr′ə al fär′ō).

Señora Arias (sen yôr′ə âr′ē əs).

Señora Endara (sen yôr′ə en där′ə).

separate Set apart; not joined. The twins have *separate* rooms. *Adjective.*
— To keep apart; divide. A fence *separates* our yard from the neighbor's yard. *Verb.*
> **sep•a•rate** (sep′ər it for *adjective;* sep′ə rāt′ for *verb*) *adjective; verb,* **separated, separating.**

several More than two, but not many. We saw *several* of our friends at the parade.
> **se•ve•ral** (sev′ər əl *or* sev′rəl) *adjective.*

shallow Not deep. The water in the pond is *shallow.*
> **shal•low** (shal′ō) *adjective,* **shallower, shallowest.**

Shang (shang *or* shông).

similar Having many but not all qualities the same; alike. Our dresses are *similar.*
> **si•mi•lar** (sim′ə lər) *adjective.*

squirm To turn or twist the body; wriggle. The children were bored and *squirmed* in their seats.
> **squirm** (skwûrm) *verb,* **squirmed, squirming.**

steep[1] Having a very sharp slope. It was difficult to ride our bicycles up the *steep* hill.
> **steep** (stēp) *adjective,* **steeper, steepest.**

---

at; āpe; fär; câre; end; mē; it; īce; pîerce; hot; ōld; sông; fôrk; oil; out; up; ūse; rüle; púll; tûrn; chin; sing; shop; thin; this; hw in white; zh in treasure. The symbol ə stands for the unstressed vowel sound in about, taken, pencil, lemon, and circus.

steep² To soak in water or another liquid. I *steeped* tea leaves in hot water.

    steep (stēp) *verb,* **steeped, steeping.**

straighten To make or become straight. The picture on the wall slanted to the left, so I *straightened* it.

    straight•en (strā′tən) *verb,* **straightened, straightening.**

strength 1. The degree of power or force; intensity. What is the *strength* of this medicine? 2. The quality of being strong; energy, power, or force. I lift weights to develop my *strength.*

    strength (strengkth *or* strength) *noun, plural* **strengths.**

stump The lower part of a tree trunk that is left when the tree has been cut down. There used to be a huge elm tree where that stump is.

    stump (stump) *noun, plural* **stumps.**

success A person or a thing that does or goes well. The party was a big *success.*

    suc•cess (sək ses′) *noun, plural* **successes.**

sukiyaki A Japanese dish made of thin strips of meat and vegetables, cooked quickly, usually at the dining table.

    su•ki•ya•ki (sü′kē yä′kē *or* skē yä′kē) *noun.*

surface The outside of a thing. The astronauts explored the *surface* of the moon.

    sur•face (sûr′fis) *noun, plural* **surfaces.**

surround To be on all sides of; form a circle around. A fence *surrounds* our yard.

    sur•round (sə round′) *verb* **surrounded, surrounding.**

T

Tao (tou *or* dou).

temperature The degree of heat or cold. Temperature is often measured with a thermometer. The *temperature* outside is going down.

    tem•per•a•ture (tem′pər ə chər) *noun, plural* **temperatures.**

thatched Covered with straw, reeds, or a similar material. The farmer's house had a *thatched* roof.

    thatched (thacht) *adjective.*

thatched

tofu A soft, white food made from mashed soybeans and formed into a cake. Tofu is used especially in Asian and vegetarian cooking. Tofu is also called bean curd.

    to•fu (tō′fü) *noun.*

tortilla A thin, round, flat bread made from water and cornmeal.
tor•til•la (tôr tē′yə) *noun, plural* **tortillas.**

Word History

The word **tortilla** comes from Mexico. In Spanish, the word *tortilla* means "little round cake."

---

treasure Money, jewels, or other things that are valuable. A chest of gold coins was part of the pirates' *treasure. Noun.*
—To think of as being of great value or importance; cherish. We *treasure* the memory of our grandparents. *Verb.*
trea•sure (trezh′ər) *noun, plural* **treasures;** *verb* **treasured, treasuring.**

treasure

triumphant Successful or victorious. Our team was *triumphant* in the game.
tri•um•phant (trī um′fənt) *adjective.*

tumble To fall in a helpless or clumsy way. When our sled tipped over, we *tumbled* out.
tum•ble (tum′bəl) *verb,* **tumbled, tumbling.**

U

underneath In a place or position below. Pack the records on top and the books *underneath. Adverb.*
—In or to a place or position lower than; under; beneath. The ball rolled *underneath* the chair. *Preposition.*
un•der•neath (un′dər nēth′) *adverb; preposition.*

V

vanish To go out of sight or existence; disappear. The airplane *vanished* above the clouds.
van•ish (van′ish) *verb,* **vanished, vanishing.**

---

at; āpe; fär; câre; end; mē; it; īce; pîerce; hot; ōld; sông; fôrk; oil; out; up; ūse; rüle; pu̇ll; tûrn; chin; sing; shop; thin; **th**is; hw in **wh**ite; **zh** in trea**s**ure. The symbol ə stands for the unstressed vowel sound in about, taken, pencil, lemon, and circus.

Yokohama A port city in east-central Japan.
Yo•ko•ha•ma (yō′kə hä′mə) *noun.*

Yokohama

ACKNOWLEDGMENTS

The publisher gratefully acknowledges permission to reprint the following copyrighted material:

"An Ant" Reprinted/Used with permission of Margaret K. McElderry Books, an imprint of Simon & Schuster Books for Young Readers, from THE ANIMALS by Michio Mado. Translated by the Empress Michiko of Japan. English translation Copyright © 1992 by the Empress Michiko of Japan.

"Animal Fact/Animal Fable" is from ANIMAL FACT/ANIMAL FABLE by Seymour Simon, illustrated by Diane de Groat. Text copyright © 1979 by Seymour Simon. Illustrations copyright © 1979 by Diane de Groat. Reprinted by permission of Crown Publishers, Inc.

Jacket illustration from the Avon Books Edition of BEEZUS AND RAMONA by Beverly Cleary, illustrated by Frederika Ribes. Text copyright © 1955 by Beverly Cleary. Reprinted by permission of William Morrow and Company, Inc.

Cover permission for BICYCLE RIDER by Mary Scioscia. Illustrations copyright © by Ed Young. Reprinted by permission of HarperCollins Publishers.

From BLACKBERRIES IN THE DARK (JACKET COVER) by Mavis Jukes with illustrations by Thomas B. Allen. Copyright © 1985 by Mavis Jukes. Illustrations Copyright © 1985 by Thomas B. Allen. Used by permission of Dell Books, a division of Bantam Doubleday Dell Publishing Group, Inc.

"Discovering Ants" from "The Life of a Worker" and "In the Ground" from DISCOVERING ANTS by Christopher O'Toole, illustrated by Wendy Meadway. Copyright © 1986 by the Bookwright Press. Copyright © 1986 Wayland (Publishers) Limited. Reprinted by permission.

"En un barrio de Los Angeles"/"In a Neighborhood in Los Angeles" from CUEPRO EN LLAMAS/BODY IN FLAMES by Francisco X. Alarcón. Copyright © 1990 by Francisco X. Alarcón. Reprinted by permission of Chronicle Books.

Cover permission for THE GIRL WHO LOVED THE WIND by Jane Yolen. Illustrations copyright © 1972 by Ed Young. Reprinted by permission of HarperCollins Publishers.

From HENRY AND THE PAPER ROUTE (JACKET COVER) by Beverly Cleary with Illustration by Louis Darling. Copyright © 1957 by Beverly Cleary. Used by permission of Dell Books a division of Bantam Doubleday Dell Publishing Group, Inc.

"Hot Plates" by Samantha Bonar. Copyright 1995 Children's Television Workshop (New York, New York). All rights reserved.

"Houses" from UP THE WINDY HILL by Aileen Fisher. Copyright © 1953 by Aileen Fisher. Copyright © renewed 1981 by Aileen Fisher. Reprinted by permission of the author.

"How Come? and What If?" from WHAT IF?: JUST WONDERING POEMS by Joy N. Hulme. Copyright © 1993 by Joy N. Hulme. Published by Boyds Mills Press.

"How My Parents Learned to Eat" is from HOW MY PARENTS LEARNED TO EAT by Ina R. Friedman, illustrated by Allen Say. Text copyright © 1984 by Ina R. Friedman. Illustrations copyright © 1984 by Allen Say. Reprinted by permission of Houghton Mifflin Co.

Cover illustration from IN COAL COUNTRY by Judith Hendershot, illustrated by Thomas B. Allen. Illustration copyright © 1987 by Thomas B. Allen. Reprinted by permission of Alfred A. Knopf, Inc.

"Invitation" reprinted with permission of Margaret K. McElderry Books, an imprint of Simon & Schuster Books for Young Readers from THERE WAS A PLACE AND OTHER POEMS by Myra Cohn Livingston. Copyright © 1988 Myra Cohn Livingston.

"The Little Painter of Sabana Grande" by Patricia Maloney Markun, illustrated by Robert Casilla. Text copyright © 1993 by Patricia Maloney Markun. Illustrations copyright © 1993 by Robert Casilla. Published Simon & Schuster Books for Young Readers. Reprinted by permission.

"Lon Po Po: A Red-Riding Hood Story from China" is from LON PO PO: A RED-RIDING HOOD STORY FROM CHINA translated and illustrated by Ed Young. Copyright © 1989 by Ed Young. Reprinted by permission of Philomel Books.

"Meet an Underwater Explorer" by Luise Woelflein reprinted from the June 1994 issue of RANGER RICK magazine, with the permission of the publisher, the National Wildlife Federation. Copyright 1994 by the National Wildlife Federation.

Cover permission for THE MOUSE AND THE MOTORCYCLE by Beverly Cleary. Copyright © 1965 by Beverly Cleary. Used by permission of Dell Books, a division of Bantam Doubleday Dell Publishing Group, Inc.

Cover permission for the Avon Books edition of MUGGIE MAGGIE by Beverly Cleary, illustrated by Frederika Ribes. Text copyright © 1990 by Beverly Cleary. Reprinted by permission of William Morrow and Company, Inc.

"Nathaniel's Rap" from NATHANIEL TALKING by Eloise Greenfield, illustrated by Jan Spivey Gilchrist. Text copyright © 1988 by Eloise Greenfield. Illustrations copyright © 1988 by Jan Spivey Gilchrist. Reprinted by permission of Scott Treimel New York on behalf of Writers and Readers Publishing and the author.

"On Granddaddy's Farm" from ON GRANDDADDY'S FARM by Thomas B. Allen. Copyright © 1989 by Thomas B. Allen. Reprinted by permission of Alfred A. Knopf, Inc.

"Opt: An Illusionary Tale" from OPT: AN ILLUSIONARY TALE by Arline and Joseph Baum. Copyright © 1987 by Arline and Joseph Baum. Used by permission of Viking Penguin, a divison of Penguin Books USA, Inc.

"Painting Mist and Fog" by Molly Bang. First appeared in CRICKET the Magazine for Children, October 1994. Copyright © The Carus Publishing Group. Reprinted by permission.

"The Patchwork Quilt" from THE PATCHWORK QUILT by Valerie Flournoy, illustrations by Jerry Pinkney. Copyright © 1985 by Valerie Flournoy, text. Copyright © 1985 by Jerry Pinkney, illustrations. Used by permission of Dial Books for Young Readers, a division of Penguin Books USA, Inc.

"Puzzle" from STREET POEMS by Robert Froman. Copyright © 1971 by Robert Froman. Reprinted by permission of the author.

Cover permission for RABBIT MAKES A MONKEY OUT OF LION by Verna Aardema, pictures by Jerry Pinkney. Copyright © 1989 by Jerry Pinkney, for pictures. Used by permission of Dial Books for Young Readers, a division of Penguin Books USA Inc.

Cover permission for RALPH S. MOUSE (JACKET COVER) by Beverly Cleary. Copyright © 1982 by Beverly Cleary. Used by permission of Dell Books, a division of Bantam Doubleday Dell Publishing Group, Inc.

Cover permission for the Avon Books edition of RAMONA AND HER FATHER by Beverly Cleary, illustrated by Frederika Ribes. Text copyright © 1975, 1977 by Beverly Cleary. Reprinted by permission of William Morrow and Company, Inc.

Text excerpt from RAMONA FOREVER by Beverly Cleary. Text copyright © 1984 by permission of Beverly Cleary. By permission of Morrow Junior Books, a division of William Morrow and Company, Inc.

Cover permission for RAMONA QUIMBY, AGE 8 (JACKET COVER) by Beverly Cleary. Copyright © 1981 by Beverly Cleary. Used by permission of Dell Books, a division of Bantam Doubleday Dell Publishing Group, Inc.

"The River Is a Piece of Sky" from THE REASON FOR THE PELICAN by John Ciardi. Copyright © 1959 by John Ciardi. Published by J. B. Lippincott Company. Reprinted by permission of the Ciardi Family.

Cover permission for RUNAWAY RALPH (JACKET COVER) by Beverly Cleary. Copyright © 1970 by Beverly Cleary. Used by permission of Dell Books, a division of Bantam Doubleday Dell Publishing Group, Inc.

"Science Magic" reprinted with the permission of Simon & Schuster Books for Young Readers from SCIENCE MAGIC by Alison Alexander and Susie Bower, illustrated by Carolyn Scrace. Text copyright (c) 1986 Susie Brower and Alison Alexander. Illustrations (c) copyright 1986 Carolyn Scrace.

"A Seeing Poem" from SEEING THINGS: A BOOK OF POEMS by Robert Froman. With lettering by Ray Barber. Copyright © 1974 by Robert Froman. Reprinted by permission of HarperCollins Publishers.

"Some Things Don't Make Any Sense At All" reprinted with permission of Atheneum Books for Young Readers, an imprint of Simon & Schuster Children's Publishing Division, from IF I WERE IN CHARGE OF THE WORLD AND OTHER WORRIES by Judith Viorst. Copyright © 1981 by Judith Viorst.

"Sunflakes" from COUNTRY PIE by Frank Asch. Copyright © 1979 by Frank Asch. Published by Greenwillow Books. Reprinted by permission of William Morrow and Company, Inc., Publishers, New York.

"The Terrible EEK" retold by Patricia A. Compton, illustrated by Sheila Hamanaka. Text copyright © 1991 by Patricia A. Compton. Illustration copyright © 1991 by Sheila Hamanaka. Published by Simon & Schuster Books for Young Readers. Reprinted by permission.

"Thinking" from AT THE TOP OF MY VOICE AND OTHER POEMS by Felice Holman. Copyright © 1970 by Felice Holman, published by Charles Scribner's Sons. Reprinted by permission of the author.

"Tinkering" by Diane Dawbar. Reprinted by permission.

Cover reprinted with the permission of Atheneum Books for Young Readers, an imprint of Simon & Schuster from TURTLE IN JULY by Marilyn Singer, illustrated by Jerry Pinkney. Illustrations copyright (c) 1989 Jerry Pinkney.

"Two Bad Ants" is from TWO BAD ANTS by Chris Van Allsburg. Copyright © 1988 by Chris Van Allsburg. Reprinted by permission of Houghton Mifflin Company.

"Under the Sunday Tree" from UNDER THE SUNDAY TREE by Eloise Greenfield, illustrated by Mr. Amos Ferguson. Text copyright © 1988 by Eloise Greenfield. Paintings copyright © 1988 by Mr. Amos Ferguson. Reprinted by permission of HarperCollins Publishers.

READING RESOURCES

COVER DESIGN: Carbone Smolan Associates
COVER ILLUSTRATION: Howard Fine (front - pig in chicken suit, David Catrow (front - crows), Kevin O'Malley (back)

DESIGN CREDITS

Carbone Smolan Associates, front matter and unit openers
Bill Smith Studio, 34-37, 80-81, 152-155, 246-249
Function Thru Form, Inc., 296-297, 300-301, 306-307, 310-315, 317
Sheldon Cotler + Associates Editorial Group, 38-63, 66-79, 84-85, 100-101
Notovitz Design Inc., 298-299, 302-305, 308-309, 316

ILLUSTRATION CREDITS

Unit 1: David Catrow, 10-11; Raphael Boguslov, 34-37; John Stevens, 38, 62-63 (typography); Mary Collier, 79; Bernard Adenet, 80-81, 152 (title); Lori Anzalone, 82-83. **Unit 2:** Howard Fine, 102-103; Sherry Bringham, 104-105, 107, 123 (calligraphy); Nancy Stahl, 126, 131-132 (b), 148-149 (b); Kathleen O'Malley, 150-151; Alejandra Sucher, 152-155; Jack Davis, 178-179; Johnathan Herbert, 182-183, 185, 187, 189, 191, 193; Jerry Zimmerman, 184, 186, 190, 192; Michael Gregniec, 194-195. **Unit 3:** Brian Selznick and Kevin O'Malley, 196-197; Iskra Johnson, 224-225 (typography); David Dunkelberger, 224-225 (bkgd.); David Diaz, 228-229; Sherry Bringham, 251 (calligraphy); Robin Milicievic, 252 (typography); Mark Herman, 254-255, 259, 264, Lisa Adams, 272-273. **Reading Resources:** Tuko Fujisaki, 300-301, 314-315; Anatoly Chernishov, 303; Felicia Telsey, 306; Paul Meisel, 307; George Poladian, 308-309; Denny Bond, 310-311; Patrick O'Brien, 312; Bob Mansfield, 313. **Glossary:** Lori Anzalone, G6, G13, G15; Bob Pepper, G7; Greg King, G8, G11, G16.

PHOTOGRAPHY CREDITS

All photographs are by the Macmillan/McGraw-Hill School Division (MMSD) except as noted below.

1: Bob Burch/Bruce Coleman. 2: l. Superstock. 3: l. Gary Braasch/Tony Stone Images. 4: b.l. Uniphoto, Inc.; t.r. William Marin, Jr./Comstock. 9: Harvey Lloyd/Stock Market. 10: b.l. Jeff Lepore/Photo Researchers, Inc. 12: b.l. Art Gingert/Comstock. 14: b.r. John Lawrence/Tony Stone Images. **Unit 1** 1: Francis Clark Westfield for MMSD. 12: t. Patricia Maloney Markun; b. Robert Casilla. 34: b. Willard Clay. 65: Michael Fredericks. 86-91: David Doubilet. 92: Doug Menuez/Reportage Stock. 93: Flip Schulke/Black Star. 94-95: Charles Nicklin/Al Giddings Images Unlimited, Inc. 95-98: Al Giddings Images Unlimited/Oceans Films. 99: background, Stuard Westmorland/Tony Stone; i. courtesy Luise Woelflein. 99: Stuart Westmorland/Tony Stone; Courtesy Luise Woelflein. **Unit 2** 124-125: Gene Ahrens/FPG International. 152: b. Oxford Scientific films. 153: t. Gerald Thompson/Oxford Scientific Films; b. P.K. Sharpe/Oxford Scientific Films. 155: t. P. & W. Ward/Oxford Scientific Films. **Unit 3** 1: Francis Clark Westfield. 224: l. Lawrence Migdale/Photo Researchers. 224-225: Lawrence Migdale/Tony Stone Images. 224: r. Ken Fisher/Tony Stone Images. 225: NC; r. Jonathan Wright/Bruce Coleman, Inc. 246: t. Ilan Rubin/Children's Television Workshop. 247: t. Esther Beaton/Terra Australis Photo ; b.l., b.r. Elaine Little. 248-249:t. Claudio Edinger/UNICEF. 248: b. Dinodia Picture Agency. 249: m.l. Viren Desai/Dinodia Picture Agency; b.l. B. Mahidhar/Dinodia Picture Agency; t. Mark Wexler/Woodfin Camp & Associates, Inc.; t.m. Karen Kasmauski/Woodfin Camp & Associates, Inc.; b.r. Envision. 249: t.m. Karen Kasmeuski/Woodfin Camp & Assoc. 250-251: Francis Clark Westfield. 251: Monica Stevenson for MMSD. **Unit 7** 1: Stephen Wilkes/The Image Bank. 1: Superstock, Inc; Bob Coxford/Stock Market; James Carmichael/The Image Bank; Rod Planck/Photo Researchers. 312: Ken C. McDonald, University of California, Santa Barbara.

The Test-Taker's HANDBOOK

★ It's almost time to take a test.

★ Are you ready?

★ You can learn some strategies.

★ You can be a better test-taker.

How to Use This Handbook

Sometimes, taking a test can make you worried. These pages will help you feel better about taking tests.

On these pages, you will find information and hints to help with different kinds of questions. You will also learn how to use what you know to make taking tests a little easier. Sometimes jotting down a few words or making up rhymes or other games will help you remember the information.

This section will help with different kinds of tests. It will help with tests that your teacher gives you. It will also help you with special tests that you might have to take.

Before you take a test, look at this section again. Each time you read it, you will remember more about taking tests. That will help you become a better test-taker.

Hints for Taking Tests

Do you think that Mark McGwire practices before a big baseball game? Sure he does!

Before you take a test, you can practice, too.

Think about these hints and strategies. Practice as many of these as you can.

It Takes Practice

Practice to get in shape before a test.

FIND OUT

★ Ask your teacher what will be on the test.

★ Will it be a book test?

★ Will it be a special test, such as the SAT?

LOOK BACK

★ Check old tests. Look at old practice papers.

★ Review what you did right.

★ Make sure you understand what you did wrong.

The trains "sound like thunder" means that they

○ make a lot of noise.

○ cause rain.

○ make the stations clean.

○ flash with bright lights.

What came first in the passage?

○ The girl jumped into the water.

○ The boy swam across the lake.

○ The puppy jumped into the lake.

○ The puppy saved the girl.

What is the main idea of the first paragraph?

○ Animals are different from people.

○ Animals can't talk.

○ Scientists know how animals act.

○ Animals work together.

Show What You Know

Do you get a little nervous when you have to take a test? That's OK — it happens to many of us.

Take a deep breath and say, "I am ready. I can do this."

Sometimes it helps to think about work you have done before.

Review reading strategies that you already know.

Oh, I remember doing one like this for homework.

TRY:

★ rereading

★ looking for clue words

★ using other words in the sentence

★ thinking about synonyms

Tick, Tick, Tick

Most tests are timed, but time can be on your side. Just play it smart.

- Take some time to study before the test.

- Skip items that you are not sure of. Come back to them later.

- Try to sum up the information. This will give you the main ideas.

Hmm, I better check this answer again.

Double Check

- When you finish an item, ask yourself these questions:

  ☐ Is my answer reasonable?

  ☐ Did I answer the question?

- Try to find the answer in the passage.

Preparing for Tests

A multiple-choice test can be the easiest kind of a test. Why? Because you know that one of the choices is the right answer. All you have to do is figure out which one it is.

○ three birds
○ two cats
○ one dog
● four ferrets

Remember to fill in only one circle for each question.

Completely fill in the correct circle for each item.

Damon and Leo stood by the lake.

"Dad, can we go swimming?" Damon asked. "The soccer game has made us really hot."

"It looks like rain," Dad answered. "Let's wait and see."

"Look," cried Theo, "the sun has come out!"

Reread the story.

1 Who wants to go swimming?
  ○ Mom
  ○ Dad
  ○ Damon and Leo
  ○ Dad and Damon

Sometimes answers don't make sense. Ignore those choices right away.

2 What have Damon and Leo just finished doing?
  ○ swimming
  ○ playing baseball
  ○ playing soccer
  ○ running around the lake

Practicing Reading Tests

Directions

Read the passage. Then read each question about the story. Choose the best answer to each question. Mark the space for the answer you have chosen.

Look for key words to help you find the answer.

Registration for Pine Valley Day Camp will be held on Saturday, May 3. The program includes daily swimming in the pond and the pool. There are nature hikes, arts and crafts, music, sports, and campfires. The camp accepts all children ages 4–12 who live in the town of Pine Valley.

Registration will be from 9:00 A.M. to 11:00 A.M. at the Pine Valley Town Hall. The sign-up fee is $10.

1 What is the meaning of registration?
○ Learning to swim
○ Singing songs
○ Signing up
○ Drawing pictures

2 Where can you register?
○ At the swimming pool
○ At the pond
○ At a campfire
○ At the town hall

Use other words in the sentence to help you learn the meaning of a new word.

Practicing Reading Tests

Directions

Read the letter. Then read each question about the letter. Choose the best answer to each question. Mark the space for the answer you have chosen.

Try to match words in the passage with words in the question.

Dear Sandy,

I'm taking Alice to the dentist. We should be home around 5:00. After you have done your homework, would you please start dinner? Spread the pizza dough onto a cookie sheet. Then pour the jar of sauce onto the dough. Sprinkle the cheese on top. I will turn on the oven when I get home.

Thanks,

Mom

3 What does spread mean in this passage?

○ A cover for a bed

○ What you put on bread

○ Cover the top of something

○ Move something apart

4 Which job will Mom do?

○ Pour the sauce

○ Turn on the oven

○ Spread the dough

○ Sprinkle the cheese

Skim the passage to help you find the answer.